DENIED

Richard Black's background is in journalism and broadcasting, including more than a decade as BBC News Environment Correspondent. He has also produced and presented science and environment programmes for BBC World Service and national radio. Since 2014 he has been Director of the Energy and Climate Intelligence Unit, an independent non-profit organisation supporting informed debate on energy and climate change. Richard lives and works in London.

"This work is of first-rate importance because it exposes the climate change denial industry in all its moral horror. It should be read attentively – in particular, by climate denying politicians on the political right who have done so much damage."
Peter Oborne, Political Columnist, *Daily Mail*

Denied

The rise and fall of climate contrarianism

Richard Black

THE REAL PRESS
www.therealpress.co.uk

Published in 2018 by the Real Press.
www.therealpress.co.uk

ISBN (print) 97819121197950
ISBN (ebooks) 97819121197943

Cover design: Andrew Hodge

For Tania, who persuaded me finally to quit stalling and do this; and for Andrew, who showed me how

And for EK – for everything

Contents

Foreword / 3
Preface / 8
Introduction: A Very British Coup / 11

1. Before the deluge / 30

2. The evidence comes in / 49

a. The climate isn't changing
b. It is changing, but it's entirely natural
c. It won't be so bad
d. We should just adapt
e. Climate science is bent
f. We can't afford it
g. The lights will go out
h. No-one else will follow us

3. Journalism eats itself / 132

4. Fake facts, cherry-picks and fantasies / 160

5. The costs of it all / 192

6. Broadcasting values / 202

7. Reality begins to bite / 214

8. Shots to the foot prove fatal / 232

Epilogia / 263

a. *Choices, 1*
b. *Red flags*
c. *Choices, 2*

References / 276
Index / 323

Foreword

By Richard Benyon MP

In about 2005, I was invited to a financial house in the City of London to hear the Australian geologist Professor Ian Plimer speak. He was then one of the high priests of scepticism on man-made climate change. His talk was heralded as the authoritative evidence-based account of why the scientific consensus was wrong.

The audience was predominately well-heeled, male, right-wing and above 60. I sat at the back looking over their heads. They were nodding, believing that at last they had found someone who proved that their natural prejudices about climate change were right. I stared at his graphs and listened to his easy confidence with one thought in my mind: for the sake of our children and all future generations, I hope you are right and the world's climate scientists wrong.

If he was right, we had nothing to fear. We would continue to see natural fluctuations in our weather, but no increase in damaging extremes. There would be no need for the Pentagon and other institutions to be concerned about the security implications of climate change. No fears of ocean levels rising, of heatwaves becoming ever more searing or crop yields falling; only a bunch of climatologists looking a little red-faced as we all got stuck back into burning as much carbon as we liked. But he was wrong.

For all of us who have accepted the weight of climate science but, when faced with obsessive climate change deniers, were brow-beaten by the almost religious zeal of their stated beliefs, here is the authentic evidence-based take-down of their core arguments. Richard Black has set out in a clear and unambiguous way how the climate change deniers are wrong.

He rightly chooses not to call them sceptics. A sceptic is a good thing to be. It shows an inquiring mind and a desire to question received wisdoms. Calling them contrarians is an elegant piece of wording. We all know contrarians. We know them at work, perhaps in our family or the golf club. They are the ones who will pick their moment and lob in a verbal hand grenade and enjoy seeing how it excites emotions.

Climate change contrarians are often very intelligent. They may include for example, former successful Chancellors of the Exchequer. As a breed they have an influence that goes way beyond the support that exists for their views in the real world and, for reasons that this book explores, have been able to use an overly pliant media to give legs to their arguments.

The members of their community have many motives – some reasonable, others perhaps less so. But they cannot escape the clear conclusions of this meticulously argued book. Nor can contrarianism's supporters in the media who continued to donate copious infusions of oxygen long beyond the point at which the real debate was over – with some, incredibly, still remaining like latter-day Canutes doggedly oblivious to the reality of man-made climate change and the success of the clean energy transition, even as the waves of evidence engulf them.

Some may wonder if a book that so eloquently examines contrarian arguments is really needed. Surely the Intergovernmental Panel on Climate Change reports are apocalyptic enough to sway all but the most reactionary dullard? I wish it were so. As this book proves, there are still too many in politics and the media who want to present arguments that fly in the face of reality.

On the political Right, acceptance of the cause and risks of climate change ought to be the natural result of Margaret Thatcher's trailblazing speeches on the subject to the UN; but still the perception has been allowed to fester that a caucus exists in the Conservative Party that does not adhere to the evidence-based view. In truth it is now a small and declining minority, as acknowledged by the contrarian Rupert Darwall who bemoaned recently:

'Environmentalism is now the official religion of the Conservative Party'. And it is inside Conservatism that contrarians have suffered their biggest defeat.

The remaining rump is matched by the coal lobby on the Left of the Labour Party and in the unions; but on both sides of politics, it is decreasingly influential. Across the Atlantic it is very different. Any one of the Republican hopefuls in the 2016 primaries would have been a voice for climate change contrarians. It has become one of those defining issues in the highly charged state of US politics. This book needs to be read there too.

I have a constituent who tells me with great regularity that continuing to burn fossil fuels is perfectly acceptable and that switching to renewable forms of energy generation is both expensive and the result of flawed science. The easiest and cheapest argument to deploy against him is to say, 'if you were me and you had someone arguing from the position of an amateur on one side and scientists who are members of the Royal Society and respected the world over, giving you an alternative view, who would you believe?'

It doesn't work. Now, however, I can refer him to this book, which not only is well researched and meticulous in its detail, but also has the virtue of being extremely readable.

This book is published at a time of political upheaval as the UK government tries to steer a path out of the European Union. Brexit consumes our media and our political discourse. To say to a political audience that there are more important things than Brexit raises eyebrows. But there are, in truth, many. Climate change is right at the top of the list. If not tackled, it presents at best the risk of huge humanitarian and economic misery and at worst a threat to our very ability to survive on this planet.

We know what to do to avoid either of these outcomes, but having the arguments at hand to make the case for action is a vital. This is a book that needed to be written, and deserves to be read.

Richard Benyon is MP for Newbury, and served as Minister for the Natural Environment 2010-13

Preface

This book has been a long time in coming – partly due to my own procrastinatory nature, partly because of an underlying belief that such a book should not, in a rational society, be needed. However... it is; and so here we are.

I am particularly grateful to a number of people who have directly contributed to this book in various ways – filling in cracks in my memory, checking my assembled evidence, and generally letting me know whether the story I've written is a compelling one. They include Keith Allott, Hugo Chandler, Jo Haigh, Catherine Happer, Zeke Hausfather, Mat Hope, Peter Jaffey, Mark Kinver, Simon Lewis, Georgina Mace, Jonathan Marshall, James Painter, Kirsty Schneeberger, Emily Shuckburgh and Phil Williamson. Plus a few other folk who need to remain, presently, anonymous: you know who you are, and I thank you.

Secondly, I want to acknowledge a debt to everyone with whom I've worked over the last four years at the Energy and Climate Intelligence Unit (ECIU): Matthew Aylott, Clare Brennan, Germana Canzi, Peter Chalkley, Matt Finch, Sepi Golzari-Munro, Pippa Henderson, John Lang, Jonathan Marshall, Anna Nicholas, Sam Richards, Luke Sheldon, George Smeeton, Helena Wright. Not to mention ECIU's Advisory Board. And to many wonderful former colleagues in the BBC and across the broader swathes of journalism. You have given me many insights and inspiration along the way, and I thank you for your good ideas and good company.

This is, however, my book rather than ECIU's – and as always, any mistakes remain my responsibility and mine alone.

A final thank-you goes to my publisher, David Boyle. David – you made easy what I feared would be impossibly hard. Thank you!

Introduction: *A very British coup*

This is the story of a coup-d'état that failed.

A coup against science, against the will of peoples from the Arctic to the Equator, against nature itself. A coup attempt that, although it has failed, may have damaged the interests of future generations and the only planet that humanity is ever likely to inhabit.

The story takes place on a Planet Earth that is becoming increasingly turbulent. The last four years have been the hottest since record-keeping began. Mountain glaciers that store drinking water for more than a billion people are melting away, slowly in the Himalayas, faster in the Andes. Arctic summer sea ice is locked in a death spiral that terminates in about 30-40 years' time, with melting permafrost set to release more warming gases into the atmosphere. Birds, insects, frogs and fish are moving away from the equator towards the poles and up mountain slopes to escape rising temperatures; sometimes, they cannot escape. Ocean water is changing from alkaline towards acidic faster than some marine life can stand. More and more often storms, heatwaves, floods, droughts and wildfires show the fingerprints of climate change, making them more frequent, longer-lasting or more intense.

This is the real world in 2018. And it concerns citizens. Between two-thirds and three-quarters of the world's population expresses concern, even alarm, on climate change. Governments and businesses are responding – quickly enough to have brought about earlier in this decade a three-year plateauing of carbon emissions unforeseen by anyone.

This is a world, then, in which nature, business, culture and discourse are being shaped by climate change. Laws are being written, investments shifted, behaviour changed and popular movements started, all in the name of responding to climate change. Most notably, virtually every government has accepted the scientific reality of man-made climate change and agreed that its main cause – the burning of fossil fuels – has to stop, on a timescale of decades.

However – on this same turbulently warming planet, there exists a parallel reality – far smaller, but influential way beyond its scale. Here, climate change does not exist. Or it does, but it is less serious than any number of other issues. Or it is serious, but the cure is worse than the disease, and the better option is just to deal with the impacts as they arise. Sometimes all three of these are held to be true simultaneously. In this world, scientists are fraudsters, ordinary folk do not care about climate change and detest renewable energy, poor countries will burn coal forever, and measures to trade in fossil fuels for a clean energy economy will return developed societies to the Stone Age.

Despite contending from time to time that they have no platform, the inhabitants of this unreal world have been remarkably effective at getting their arguments heard in high places. Their beliefs have been debated in parliaments and declaimed in courts. In places, their proponents have dominated the media commentariat. Now, their highest profile recruit ever, Donald Trump, sits on the throne of the world's most powerful nation, dismissing climate change with the same casual mien with which he questions why the US admits non-white people. As a result, some Unrealists claim that they have won. Trump will turn back the clock on coal and oil, they say. He will nuke international climate change treaties and build a wall against the human tide of public opinion – and the rest of the world will have no option but to follow.

Were this true, it would be the most Pyrrhic of victories. There would be little enough to celebrate in ushering in a world where, science indicates, yields of staple crops are likely to fall even as the number of hungry mouths increases, where natural miracles like coral reefs wither and die, where rising seas threaten the integrity of capital city after capital city.

Fortunately, it is not true. In the real world, the Unrealists, the contrarians, have lost the argument. In China, in India, in western Europe, across the Pacific, even in the US itself, seismic shifts are taking place that are moving society away from untrammelled fossil fuel use towards a future of clean energy, smart tech, electric cars and, accordingly, healthier lives. Existential concern about the impacts of climate change is one driver – alongside, now, simple economics, and competition to own the industries of the near future rather than those of the recent past.

In the real world, investors now put more money into electricity generation from wind and sun than from coal and gas – and renewable energy is or soon will be cheaper than the old alternatives in virtually every nation. In the real world, governments increasingly take the view that tackling climate change will be good for their economies. Military top brass plan for a greater risk of conflict if it is not tackled, doctors scan the horizon for the advent of new disease epidemics, religious leaders highlight increasing pressures on the world's poor, businesses analyse climate risks to their supply chains, wealth funds withdraw their money from coal-connected companies, and young Britons see climate change as a more important issue than crime.[1]

Ten years ago, the picture was far less clear. Then, the network of contrarians had much to say and much to ask that was useful. They probed the practices of science in a way that led to positive reforms. They queried journalism, forcing those of us involved in it to be more precise and more rigorous in our reporting.

Yet if a week is a long time in politics, a decade can bring a sea-change in both scientific understanding and economic realities. The integrity of climate science emerged intact from the many inquiries into it. Whereas the pace of global warming appeared to have stalled for a while, it has since accelerated again with a vengeance – and science now understands much more clearly why such accelerations and decelerations occur. Nation after nation, led by the UK, has shown that it is perfectly possible to grow an economy and reduce carbon emissions simultaneously.

The side-benefits of adopting clean technologies in electricity generation and motoring are clearer than ever. Public support for clean energy, in the UK and elsewhere, is startlingly high. And despite Donald Trump's as yet unfulfilled promise to withdraw, the

Paris Agreement shows unequivocally that the vast majority of governments see a transition to a clean energy economy as being in their national interest.

To sum it up, you could say that the events of the last decade have proven contrarians wrong on all of their core arguments. And you would be almost entirely right.

Many coup attempts involve mercenaries, and this one is no different. The ranks of climate change contrarians include a host of public relations executives and a handful of scientists paid by the fossil fuel industry to attack and undermine the evidence base.

There are politicians (especially in the US) who owe their offices to coal and oil money. And – notably in the Arabian Gulf – there are states whose economies rest on oil and gas, which therefore have the most existential of economic incentives to downplay climate change.

But these folk are perhaps less important – and certainly less interesting – than those who come to the contrarian camp for non-financial reasons. This book is about them. It is not strictly speaking 'their story'; I am not particularly interested in their 'life journeys' and how they arrived at their rhetorical positions, but I am interested in how they chose to deploy their influence and in why large sections of the media, for an overly long time, gave them credence.

In both the media and politics, their star is now undoubtedly waning, for reasons that begin with weight of evidence. And that decline is, I think, the most interesting story of all.

If the US is the epicentre of financed climate denial, the UK has consistently been the hub of what you might call 'conviction contrarianism'. Therefore this ends up being largely a UK story, albeit one that has global implications. From its hub, spokes have connected out to other nations, especially the former 'white dominions' of Canada, Australia, New Zealand and the United States. At times Britain's conviction contrarianism has melded with the financed denial of Washington, Alberta and Queensland, but has often been in the intellectual vanguard. Part of the movement's success was due to the global reach of and respect for UK news media, which is read and re-transmitted in nations from South Africa to St Kitts.

There are many contenders for the title of Contrarian-in-Chief, but one for whom one can make an excellent case is Nigel Lawson. Chancellor of the Exchequer and Energy Secretary under the premiership of Margaret Thatcher, Lawson re-cast himself once clad in peer's ermine as a serious, rigorous, economically literate scrutineer who had run his rule over the various dimensions of climate change and found them wanting.

The group that Lawson founded in 2009, the Global Warming Policy Foundation (GWPF) and its later spin-off the Global Warming Policy Forum,[a] sits at the centre

---

[a] The Foundation was created as an 'educational charity' in 2009. The Forum was created as a wholly-owned subsidiary 'campaigning arm' in 2014 after the Charity Commission ruled that the Foundation had 'promoted a particular position on global warming'

of a web of influence which, at its peak, penetrated deep into the British media and political establishments and framed most of the important conversations on climate change.

Over a three-month period either side of the 2009 Copenhagen Summit, Lawson and his director Dr Benny Peiser chalked up more than 80 mentions between them in the UK's ten main newspapers. By contrast the most-quoted contrarian scientist, Australian geologist Professor Ian Plimer, garnered just 13.[2] The UK media's set of climate-contrarian commentators all still have links to GWPF, and several other self-styled 'think-tanks' that question the case for a clean energy transition share or nestle close by its premises at 55 Tufton Street, a short walk from Parliament. Its reach extends outside the UK; its reports have been presented to US Congressional committees, and articles by its affiliates re-printed in media across the 'white dominions'.

Small in funding terms but immensely well-connected, future generations of politics students may come to regard GWPF as a case study in how to run a campaign that is highly effective politically without a scintilla of public engagement or – as I will show later – public support.

Ten years ago – a year before founding GWPF – Lawson published a book, *An Appeal to Reason: A Cool*

---

https://assets.publishing.service.gov.uk/government/uploads/system/uploads/attachment_data/file/432482/ocr_the_global_warming_policy_foundation.pdf

Look at Global Warming. In accessible (and to some, persuasive) prose, he outlines the canonical arguments against acting to reduce greenhouse gas emissions: climate change will not be that serious (and in some cases people will benefit), scientific opinion is divided and the UN's international science panel alarmist, we can simply adapt to climate impacts, no other countries will transform their energy base even if Britain does, combatting climate change will hurt the world's poor, switching away from fossil fuels will ruin our economy, and adoption of renewable energy will mean the lights going out.

In the same year, the UK Parliament passed the Climate Change Act – the first piece of legislation anywhere in the world to enshrine a target for cutting greenhouse gas emissions in law. The story it encapsulates is almost the exact opposite of Lawson's: science has reliably painted a picture of a world where climate change poses increasing risks to societies and nature, the cost of a clean energy transition will be affordable and amply justified, and many nations are already moving in that direction, albeit at highly varying speeds.

The counterpoint of Lawson's book and the Climate Change Act emerging in the same year allows us now to set the two visions alongside each other and simply ask: which proved to be correct? No political or historical baggage is needed for the evaluation. We can leave ideologies at the door. Labour or Conservative, Brexiteer or Remainer, free-marketeer or state intervener; evidence is evidence, and the decade has provided a wealth of it with which we can now see which set of beliefs has stood the test of time and which has not.

The harsh truth for the contrarians is that their canonical arguments turned out to be wrong. All have been overtaken by evidence – often coming from real-world events, sometimes from new research. On only two of the core arguments does a smattering of truth remain:

- Some elements of the clean energy economy are still more expensive than the fossil fuel-powered alternatives
- It is not clear that all nations will pursue a clean energy transition quickly enough to meet the global warming targets that they have pledged to meet.

On all the others, as I will show, *An Appeal to Reason* stands now, not as a beacon of rationality shining through a smog of green delusion, but as testament to humankind's prodigious capacity for advancement. Within a single decade, science, technology and the international body politic have answered the questions that Nigel Lawson posed and overcome the objections he raised. It is a wonderfully optimistic turn of events.

Science cannot be immune from society's scrutiny. The donning of a white coat does not transform a person into an oracle or a saint. It is right that scientific findings in policy-relevant fields such as climate change are subject to more rigorous inquiry than those that tell us interesting but less immediately relevant stories about the lineage of dinosaurs or the interior of neutron stars.

It is right that journalists probe claims of environment groups which, for example, sometimes overplay the links between climate change and extreme weather. There are, too, examples of ill-thought-through policies that have ended up doing more harm than good – and it is entirely right that journalists interrogate them, and that civil society is not allowed to sweep them under the rug.

Ten years ago, both science and the body politic had some serious questions to answer on climate change – and sometimes the answers cupboard looked pretty threadbare. Why had the rate of global warming slowed down? How much would swapping cheap coal power for expensive renewables cost? A year after *An Appeal to Reason*'s publication, still more questions emerged. Did a tranche of hacked scientists' emails show they had been conspiring to misrepresent their findings? Were parts of a UN assessment based on a green campaign group's dodgy dossier? And did governments really care anyway, given that the Copenhagen summit, the occasion at which when they were supposed to take joint ownership of the problem, ended in a mass race for the exit with each world leader touting a fig leaf of his or her choosing?

But time moves on – and so does evidence. When that happens, a real sceptic moves on too. A genuinely sceptical approach means turning scepticism on your own beliefs as well as those of others. This is something that good scientists do. It is harder for politicians – but even here, 'I was wrong' is possible.

Despite the mound of evidence on all of the

canonical contrarian points, those at the core of 'conviction contrarianism' have not fundamentally changed their positions. The decade has brought irrefutable evidence that the climate is changing. There is no longer any serious dispute that fossil fuel burning is the main culprit – in fact it would be hard to think of any scientific notion that has been as amply tested and as solidly confirmed. The cost of renewable energy has plummeted faster than anyone, even Greenpeace, foresaw. For those who follow money rather than science, evidence rests in the flight of capital from coal into renewables, battery storage and electric vehicles.

These real-world stories are far more dynamic and exhilarating than the turgid and negative ones they replaced. But they are not ones that contrarians acknowledge. The record for the 'warmest year' is broken three years in a row and the 'global warming pause' is over. The contrarian response is to claim that all the heat came from an El Niño event and the pause is intact. The price of renewable energy contracts goes through the floor; the contrarian response is to argue that the prices are not 'real'. The Chinese government pledges to peak its carbon emissions by 2030; contrarians ignore it, maintaining that the nation will build hundreds of new coal-fired power stations even though it clearly will not.

It has all become rather ridiculous. The contrarian establishment, which only a decade ago played a credible and useful role highlighting genuine areas of doubt, now resembles nothing so much as a rhetorical version of Monty Python's Black Knight as it desperately tries to protect its intellectual hinterland. 'Three record warmest years? 'Tis but a scratch. Lights staying on as coal-fired power stations close? Just a flesh wound. I'll bite your legs off with my "hidden costs of renewables" argument.'

As evidence accumulates, maintaining both a doctrinal position and credibility becomes an impossible juggling act. One has to choose.

If contrarian commentators and contrarian arguments have been proven wrong, do they still matter – in the UK Parliament, in its media, and to other nations?

I would argue that they do. Their influence is retreating, but their voice is still present in political and media discourse to an extent that far exceeds either the validity of their arguments or the degree to which they represent public opinion.

There is, too, the indisputable point that media coverage on issues of public importance, including those involving science, matters. Measles cases in the UK rose in the aftermath of the MMR vaccine controversy, from 50-100 per year in the late 1990s to more than a thousand per year a decade later.[3] This summer saw the World Health Organisation reporting 41,000 cases and 37 deaths across Europe.

Public Health England said: 'The majority of cases we are seeing are in teenagers and young adults who missed out on their MMR vaccine when they were children.'[4] There is evidence that misleading media coverage of the MMR episode contributed to the comeback of this once vanquished disease.[5] These are real children, contracting a real disease with serious implications, extending to disability and even death.

Another example is HIV/AIDS. In the 1990s, the *Sunday Times* newspaper kept the argument that the virus did not cause the disease alive beyond the point at which the scientific case was really unanswerable. In South Africa, Thabo Mbeki's government refused to support use of anti-retroviral drugs even as AIDS cases extended into the millions, instead promoting a 'treatment' of lemon juice and garlic. Statisticians calculate that the delay cost 330,000 lives.[6] There is anecdotal support for the view that 'AIDS denial' in a blue-chip British newspaper bolstered Mbeki's case as he found excuse after excuse to deny his people drugs that would keep them alive.[7]

On these issues, prolonging the 'debate' beyond the point at which the evidence was in had material consequences. Climate change is no different. As with MMR and HIV/AIDS, there are no brownie points here for being on the wrong side of history. Robust journalistic scrutiny is a key ingredient of a healthy society. Contrarianism-signalling is not.

The media looms large in this story. Partly this is because journalism is my background – it is the part of the story I know best. But the main reason is because the climate contrarian campaign has always been focused on influencing the media.

Some contrarian memes play on our desire for familiarity, stability and convenience – life would after all be easier were there no imperative to change the energy system that has sustained humanity's progress since the Industrial Revolution. Others are stories of jeopardy, notably 'the lights will go out' or 'bills are set to soar', which for years proved irresistible – and in whose promotion contrarians were often joined by interested incumbents in the energy sector.

For years, parts of the media lapped them up without a hint of scepticism. Some went much further and actively promoted them, despite them being in diametric opposition to reality – and, more interestingly, to the views of their readers. Reading through a draft of this book, a friend, who has never lived or worked in the UK, observed that 'the level of media collusion is extraordinary.' 'Collusion' is a strong word; but by the time you have read to the final pages, you may well find yourself agreeing with her.

If the point of the exercise was to sway public opinion, it has failed spectacularly. Support for action to curb climate change, for subsiding renewable energy and energy efficiency, and indeed for the Climate Change Act, has proved substantial and enduring. In politics, it is a different story. For years MPs would regularly read in prime-time papers that the Earth was not getting any warmer. That climate science was bent, or at least incompetent. They would read that a clean energy transition was unaffordable, unworkable, unnecessary and unpopular. That Africans were being kept poor by western environmental groups denying them coal-fired power stations. That Britain was the only country in the world trying to enact such a transition.

A key aspect of the approach was to persuade politicians – and presumably the papers' editors – that public opinion was exactly the opposite of what it really was. The British public has never hated wind turbines – but if favoured columnists said often enough that they did, the perception would grow, with an inevitable impact on policymaking.

One suspects – though it is impossible to prove – that given the global reach of some British media, UK contrarianism has impacted some governments' approach to climate change. In the UK itself, its main impact has been to muddy and confuse energy policy; there is circumstantial evidence that it has exerted an upwards pressure on energy bills, despite the claim of many contrarian commentators to care about lowering them. And it has clearly helped to confuse both the public and politicians.

So this is why contrarianism matters. You may disagree with my choice of the term 'coup', but I find it highly applicable for a situation in which black is claimed to be white, and where those claims can steer policymaking in a direction antithetical to the interests of British and global citizens. To be sure, a coup of memes rather than machine-guns – narratives, not napalm. A bloodless coup; though not, perhaps, a victimless one.

If coup attempt it was, it has failed. Large chunks of the media that until recently flew the contrarian flag, either passively or with relish, have now quietly taken it down. The few that have not now stand out, open to (and actually receiving) ridicule. You cannot hope to conceal a mountain of reality with rhetoric once it grows beyond a certain point, however fine your use of language and however elite your connections.

Before I dive into the main body of this book, a few other points need making.

The first concerns terminology. The terms most

often used to describe Lord Lawson and his fellow travellers are 'climate sceptics' and 'climate deniers'.

I am uncomfortable with both, for different reasons. Being sceptical, in science, in politics and in journalism, is a virtue, and the appellation must be earned. We cannot legitimately bestow the term 'sceptic' on a group of people who typically ignore large slices of the evidence while embracing much that is manifestly wrong. The label 'denier' sits uncomfortably for other reasons – one is its echo of holocaust denial, the other is that many people in this camp (including Lawson) do not deny the existence of man-made climate change, but instead question its severity and the measures proposed for constraining it.

In this book I am going to stick, generally, with 'contrarian'. As well as carrying neither the positive connotation of 'sceptic' nor the negative one of 'denier', I think it is more accurate. Certainly the dictionary definition of 'A person who opposes or rejects popular opinion' fits well. More pertinently, the fundamental USP of many in this camp seems to combine 'I am cleverer than the experts' with 'thinking differently is a good thing'. And this, I think, defines contrarianism rather neatly.

In addition, I deliberately do not distinguish between the various nuances of stance inside the contrarian or 'sceptic' community. The Oxford academic Dr James Painter distinguishes four basic types:[8]

- Trend sceptics, who doubt the evidence for climate change
- Attribution sceptics, who doubt a human cause

- Impact sceptics, who doubt that climate change will be serious
- Policy sceptics, who question the 'solutions' to climate change.

In reality, one frequently finds more than one colour of contrarianism rolled up in the same individual, and that arguments morph chameleon-like from one to the other. More fundamentally, whether you deny climate change is happening, argue it is largely benign or campaign against clean energy systems on reliability grounds, the potential impact on policymaking is similar. And while it is entirely possible to accept evidence on climate change and distrust renewable energy, or to applaud renewables while distrusting climate science, it is remarkable how often climate and energy contrarianism are rolled up in the same organisations and individuals.[b]

Secondly, two other bits of terminology. 'Climate change' or 'global warming'? Although the terms are often used interchangeably, they should not be. 'Global warming' properly refers to the temperature rise, usually taken as an average across the Earth's surface, which is the most direct consequence of greenhouse gas emissions. By contrast, 'climate change' is the much wider set of effects including the warming of ocean and land, sea-level rise, changes to weather patterns, ice-

---

[b] This linkage was demonstrated a couple of years back when John Constable, for years the head of the anti-renewable energy Renewable Energy Foundation, went to work with GWPF

sheet melt, and so on. Thus global warming is really just one aspect of climate change. Generally speaking, I will use 'climate change' unless I am referring specifically to the global average surface temperature rise, in which case I will use 'global warming'.

Thirdly, a couple of technical matters. One is that for ease of reading, I am going to omit mention of the baseline year against which emission cuts are pledged and measured. Unless noted otherwise, the baseline year is always 1990, the year generally used within the United Nations climate convention and in the UK Climate Change Act.

The other concerns references. Some scientific journals such as *Nature*, and some newspapers such as *The Times*, hold content behind a paywall. Whenever the material concerned has been posted on a different website with open access, that is the link I use.

Fourthly, I am concentrating here on the last decade. Thus you will not find here a detailed dissection of the 'hockey-stick controversy' or the scientific validity of Al Gore's *An Inconvenient Truth*. Quite enough has been written about those episodes already. Added to which, the world has moved on: if you would argue that the validity or not of contrarian claims depends on events that took place more than a decade ago, I would say it is time for you to find some new arguments.

The final point is rather more personal. I would be delighted if Nigel Lawson, Matt Ridley, Christopher Booker and the rest of the contrarian elite were right, and the near-entirety of the world's climate scientists and governments wrong. It would mean a simpler world for me in the rest of my lifetime, a better life for my children and, if I am fortunate enough to have them, my grandchildren.

It would temper the urgency for a transition to a clean energy economy – even though many of the other reasons for the transition, such as reducing air pollution and simple economics, would still push it forwards. It would increase political space for dealing with other major issues of our time, national and global. It would remove one reason for the existential anxiety that so many young people feel about the world they are inheriting.

Yet ... there is not a shred of evidence that they are right. Splenetic newspaper columns and grand speeches in the House of Lords cannot stand beside the accumulated evidence base, from science, businesses, investors and public opinion, that climate change presents serious risks that we do not have to take. And the contrarians' dogged adherence to their canonical arguments even as the world changes around them is exactly why their grip on the levers of government has weakened so far as to be almost imperceptible.

But first – having said that I will not be diving back into ancient history, I do need to take something of a run-up to the last decade.

1
Before the deluge

In the middle of the 2000s, it seemed as though the 'climate change debate' really was over. All the world's nations had agreed the United Nations Kyoto Protocol in 1997; and although President George W. Bush had taken the US out of the Protocol, it entered into force in 2005 after years of wrangling about issues as arcane as the definition of a tree.[c]

This meant that all developed nations bar the US now had targets to limit, and in most cases reduce, their greenhouse gas emissions. In the same year, UK Prime Minister Tony Blair, as President of the G8 group of nations, made climate change and Africa's economic development his twin priorities for the group's summit at Gleneagles, emerging with an agreement in which all leaders (including Bush) acknowledged the reality of man-made climate change and pledged to lead the world towards a low-carbon economy.[9]

The following year saw publication of the Stern Review on the Economics of Climate Change, commissioned by Blair and his Chancellor Gordon

---

[c] Arcane but necessary – this has to be agreed in order to make any systematic assessment of deforestation, afforestation or reforestation possible

Brown.[10] Its central conclusion was that tackling climate change was going to be a lot cheaper in the long run than not doing so. Some other economists including Nigel Lawson disputed that conclusion, but the Review's political impact in the UK and globally was significant. It featured heavily at that year's UN climate summit in Nairobi, for which the central theme was the existential threat that climate change posed to African societies already in a fragile state of development.

Then, in 2007, came the latest Assessment Report from the Intergovernmental Panel on Climate Change (IPCC), the UN organisation that collates and distils evidence on the science and economics of climate change.[11] This report was the fourth in a series dating back to 1990. Although it broadly followed similar lines to its forerunners, its conclusions this time round were tighter, backed up by nearly 3,000 pages of evidence collated and sifted by specialists from 130 countries.

The IPCC made a better fist of presenting it too, its flamboyant Indian chair Rajendra Pachauri combining elegant use of language with the moral authority of the developing world.[d] Its central conclusions – that 'warming of the climate system is unequivocal', human activities were more than 90 per cent likely to be the main cause, and severe and escalating risks lay ahead unless greenhouse gas emissions were constrained – seemed unlikely to be seriously contradicted, despite

---

[d] His personal moral authority did not survive sexual harassment charges filed in 2016 – but that issue was not known at the time

challenges emerging in the increasingly febrile contrarian blogosphere.

So – the science was apparently 'in'. So was the economics, while the G8 outcome suggested that the world's most potent developed nations, with the exception of the US under 'Dubya', were also persuaded that more serious action on climate change was needed. In the court of public opinion, the case was unanswerable. A survey for BBC World Service across 21 nations – rich and poor, north and south, east and west – found that 79 per cent of the world's citizens accepted the evidence of a human cause for climate change. Ninety per cent wanted their leaders to find a solution – 65 per cent saying 'it is necessary to take major steps starting very soon'.[12]

And so in December 2007, delegates from 195-odd countries met for the annual United Nations climate summit, in Bali, Indonesia, and agreed that within two years they would strike a new deal that would address climate change more comprehensively than the Kyoto Protocol. Known as the Bali Roadmap, this showed that despite the reservations of the US, Russia, Japan, China, Saudi Arabia and a few others, there was a general will to make progress. And indeed, how could it be otherwise, given that all those governments had just endorsed the IPCC's Fourth Assessment Report and the picture it painted of escalating risks ahead?

In the UK, things were also moving fast. Gordon Brown, now Prime Minister, was unequivocally tied to the logic of accelerating action on climate change through his sponsorship of the Stern Review. Conservative Party leader David Cameron was busy 'detoxifying the Tory brand', including putting wind turbines on his roof and travelling to the Arctic to hug a husky. Not everyone in his party believed in 'voting blue to go green', as the campaign slogan had it, but this young and telegenic leader seemed capable of delivering success at the ballot box, which always tends to mute internal party criticism.

Meanwhile, the environment group Friends of the Earth had come forward with a daring proposal for a world-first Climate Change Act. The government should, they argued, use science and considerations of equity to calculate how much the UK should reduce its greenhouse gas emissions by the middle of the century in order to play its 'fair share' in keeping global warming below 2 degrees Celsius.[e] It should then set that target in law, and establish an independent advisory and scrutineering body tasked with ensuring that the UK cut emissions along the most economically efficient trajectory.

On many occasions, such an apparently radical idea would have perished on the stony ground of *realpolitik*. But given David Cameron's desire to use the environment as a 'detoxifying' tool, the Conservatives in opposition were persuaded to support the idea; and the Labour government then had no choice but to go along with it, as they could not let themselves be 'out-greened' by the Conservatives. Support from most minor parties was guaranteed.

Outside Parliament, the Climate Change Bill received backing from a remarkable array of civil society groups including the National Trust, the RSPB,

---

[e] The international target then generally agreed

UNISON and the Women's Institute, while businesses including Shell and BP wrote to the Prime Minister asking for 'a transition to a low-carbon economy'.[13]

And so, in 2008, the Climate Change Act passed through Parliament on a remarkable cross-party consensus forged by political figures including Tim Yeo, Lord (David) Puttnam, Lord (John) Deben and the Miliband brothers. It committed future governments to reducing UK emissions by at least 80 per cent by 2050 and set up an independent advisor and watchdog, the Committee on Climate Change. The final vote in the Commons was astonishing – 483 MPs in favour, just three against.

On 26 November, six months after Nigel Lawson published *An Appeal to Reason*, the Climate Change Act received Royal Assent. The UK became the first nation in the world to set a greenhouse gas emission reduction target in national law.

For anyone opposed to constraining climate change, events on the other side of the Atlantic were even more alarming. A young dynamic Democrat named Barack Obama trounced his Republican rival John McCain in the November 2008 Presidential election, and seemed likely to apply his 'yes, we can' motto to climate change as an integral part of an outward- and forward-looking Presidency very different from the 'no, we won't' approach of the Bush years.

To a journalist whose bread and butter issue was climate change, these were heady times indeed. At the BBC, I sometimes joked about the natural habitat of the environment correspondent being the end of the news bulletin – delivering a story about ladybirds or remediation of the Cliffs of Dover, which allowed the

Today Programme presenter a tiny chuckle in the voice before diving into the serious interview ahead.

Now, the habitat had grown markedly. Birds and butterflies were still in; but Tony Blair's G8 move, the Stern Review, the IPCC report, the Bali Roadmap and the Climate Change Act obliged editors to see climate change as the serious issue that we science and environment specialists had long known it to be. And the direction of travel, both in the UK and internationally, appeared set. Science would always refine knowledge and throw up new discoveries, governments' enthusiasm for cutting emissions would wax and wane; but broadly, the die was cast – the world was going to do this.

But, below the surface, trouble was brewing.

For one thing, the Earth did not seem to be warming up at the same speed as previously. At least, that was the story told by a record of the average temperature at the Earth's surface known as HadCRUT.[14] Maintained by scientists at the UK Met Office and the University of East Anglia (UEA), this is one of the three most important records of global temperature.[f] The story that 'global warming has stopped' began to circulate on contrarian blogs and occasionally made it to mainstream media.[15] Then came new research indicating that the 'pause' in surface warming might last for another decade.[16]

---

[f] The other two are the GISSTEMP record produced by NASA and the NOAAGlobalTemp record from the US National Oceanic and Atmospheric Agency (NOAA). Others have become more important since 2008, and will be covered later

The 'pause' or 'hiatus' appeared to start in 1998, which saw a strong El Niño event, when heat released from the Pacific Ocean into the atmosphere warmed the globe. So in one sense it was not surprising that the following years were cooler than 1998. But it was a perplexing turn of events – and although scientists had legitimate arguments as to why it did not change the overall picture of climate change, they often struggled to communicate those arguments effectively. Sceptics – let me use that word here, as it is merited – were far more effective at communicating their concerns, and so the hiatus became a 'thing'.

There was more. In 2007, I published a series of 10 articles on the BBC News website on climate scepticism, some written by me and some by guest contributors.[17] As a result, I had struck up a number of conversations with contrarians, and was copied in on some large email chains. One of the chains contained about 70 people, from both sides of the Atlantic.[g]

I presume that not everyone on the chain knew who I was, because a discussion began on the idea of establishing a new contrarian campaign group to take on the orthodoxy. At the time, a number of such groups were active, in the US, UK and Australia; but clearly, given the prevailing direction of political travel, none was having the cut-through necessary to take policymaking in the direction they wanted. The idea under discussion was to have a new organisation up

---

[g] Some of the individuals were familiar to anyone who followed climate contrarianism closely at the time, but none were household names; neither Lord Lawson nor Benny Peiser was among them

and running ahead of the 2009 UN summit and the new global agreement it was due to deliver. They noted that to be effective, it would need to command media attention and would need to have a convincing and high-profile chair. Among the names proposed as a possible chair was that of Lord Lawson.

Eventually – I suppose – someone twigged that copying in a journalist on these emails was not a very smart idea, and I was quietly removed from the chain. But it was an interesting insight, given what happened a year and a half later: the launch of a new organisation questioning the seriousness of climate change and the case for decarbonisation, which within its first week in existence gained huge media attention for what appeared to be a major 'smoking gun' story.

Let me now fast-forward to the second half of 2009. We were heading towards what was due to be the seminal United Nations climate change summit in Copenhagen, when governments were supposed to tie up a new comprehensive global agreement as they had pledged in Bali. We knew the summit would be seminal because world leaders kept telling us so. Gordon Brown said it had to reach an agreement that would 'change the course of history'.[18] Australia's Prime Minister Kevin Rudd said it 'represents a critical moment' in efforts to tackle climate change,[19] while for French President Nicolas Sarkozy, failure in Copenhagen 'would be a catastrophe for each and every one of us'.[20]

In reality, negotiations were not going well, for a number of reasons. One was the sheer complexity of the draft agreement, which at one stage ran to nearly 200 pages.[21] This was a reflection of the politicking between various blocs and countries, and the different interests at play. Tensions between developed and developing countries were rising. There was also an emerging divide between one bloc of developing countries primarily concerned about impacts of climate change, and another that prioritised the traditional 'right to develop using fossil fuels' argument. Brazil, South Africa, India and China had formed a powerful new grouping, the BASICs, which largely ran the politics of the official developing world bloc, the G77/China.[22] Barack Obama was not providing the degree of climate change leadership that progressive nations and environmental groups had hoped for, preferring instead to make healthcare reform his first-term signature issue.

The Danish host government made some appalling decisions, including sacking its well-regarded lead negotiator, Thomas Becker, weeks before the summit.[23] Prime Minister Lars Lokke Rasmussen was rumoured to be preparing a secret text that would be slapped on the table if and when negotiations on the official one stalled – a real trust-breaking story, which turned out to be true.[24]

A month or so before the summit, European negotiators and then ministers admitted that the summit would not deliver the all-inclusive deal that had been promised two years earlier.[25]

For environment journalists, the Copenhagen summit had really been the only story in town for six months. Announcements from governments and businesses came thick and fast. Research reports flooded in. The politics of the impending summit first promised increasing returns, then slowly unravelled. Like many other environment correspondents, I and my BBC colleagues were covering the relentless flow of daily news while simultaneously preparing features that would be published during the summit to give audiences the background and context they would need to make sense of it, given that the summit was probably going to be the lead story for most of a fortnight.

On 20 November, just over a fortnight before the UN talks opened, my BBC colleague Mark Kinver became aware of a story emerging on climate contrarian websites. A large tranche of files had, apparently, been obtained from a computer server in the Climatic Research Unit (CRU) at the University of East Anglia (UEA). As one 'parent' of the HadCRUT temperature record, CRU is one of the most important research units in the world for understanding how the Earth is warming. Scientists there assemble temperature data from weather stations and other sources to provide a dataset that is used by governments, the UN and other scientists as a key piece of evidence for global warming.

The files taken included information on how CRU director Professor Phil Jones and his colleagues processed data, and emails between CRU scientists and their peers in other universities.

Whoever had obtained the files decided not to release them all. Instead, a set of just over 4,500 was posted on a few select websites, together with a digest. Taken at face value, this digest appeared to show that scientists had colluded with each other to rig the evidence – cherry-picking and distorting research findings in order to keep alive a picture of rising global temperatures that they knew not to be true.

For a journalist, it was a troublesome story. We could not know at the time if all the emails were real, we had no idea who had released them and how, and there was absolutely no context given for the statements being highlighted. Nevertheless, Mark and I decided to write the story,[26] making the BBC News website the first mainstream media outlet in the world to report on the affair that would become known as 'ClimateGate'.[h]

Just three days later, on Monday 23 November, in the House of Lords, Nigel Lawson launched the Global Warming Policy Foundation.[27] Its first act, that same day, was to call for an inquiry into what it described as 'very serious issues and allegations that reach to the heart of scientific integrity and credibility'.[28]

The stunning coincidence of the email release and the GWPF launch happening within a week of each other, shortly before the UN summit that was supposed to deliver a new global climate agreement, gave the organisation and its leader a dynamite story with which they could make a mark. Papers carried news stories about GWPF's launch, and *The Times* of 23 November ran an article penned by Lawson, concluding with the call for an inquiry into the emails.[29]

---

[h] 'ClimateGate' is the term most used in current parlance, but – as with 'climate denier' – I will not use it as it is innately pejorative. For a full account of the episode, see Fred Pearce's excellent and very readable account *The Climate Files*

Whereas Lawson was careful enough to suggest that 'there could be an innocent explanation', others were not as circumspect. In a spate of media articles emerging the weekend following, Christopher Booker in his *Sunday Telegraph* column unequivocally labelled the affair a 'maze of skulduggery' and 'the greatest scientific scandal of our age'.[30]

In the *Express*, former MP Neil Hamilton praised Lord Lawson's plan to 'even up the debate', telling us that climate scientists 'routinely behave like political spin-doctors', carbon dioxide is not a pollutant, and the global temperature was falling.[31] Meanwhile in Canada's National Post newspaper, former *Telegraph* proprietor Conrad Black wrote that 'carbon emissions are not the principal factor in global warming' and 'the ice-caps are not melting', concluding his article with an encomium to the 'immensely respected' former Chancellor.[32] His article's title, 'The Great Green Fraud', carries a fair degree of presumably unintentional irony, given that Lord Black was at the time in prison for obstruction of justice and – er – fraud.[33]

And so the email hack became a second major climate change story running alongside the fast-approaching UN summit. It was joined by another story, somewhat predictably dubbed 'HimalayaGate', which emerged just before the summit.

On 13 November, the eminent science journalist Pallava Bagla had related in the journal *Science* that an Indian government report contradicted the IPCC's picture of a continent where 'India's 10,000 or so Himalayan glaciers are shrinking rapidly in response to climate change'.[34] Bagla highlighted a claim in the

Fourth Assessment Report that was obviously wrong – that the likelihood of Himalayan glaciers 'disappearing by the year 2035 and perhaps sooner is very high if the Earth keeps warming at the current rate'.

Three weeks later, Canadian glaciologist Graham Cogley told Bagla in an article for the BBC News website that the source of the 2035 date had been a report by environment group WWF, which in turn cited an earlier article in *New Scientist* magazine.[35] IPCC chief Pachauri did his organisation no favours by dismissing the Indian government report as 'voodoo science' – which it clearly was not, especially with respected scientists such as Cogley backing up the overall case.

And then came the Copenhagen summit itself, which those of us who were there for the entire fortnight are unlikely ever to forget. Some long-time observers contend that it was not in the end a failure. They argue that it saw the death of a 'Kyoto Protocol' approach to negotiating emission cuts that was always going to lead to a political dead-end, and instead ushered in a more politically realistic modality that in the end made the Paris Agreement possible.[i]

---

[i] The approach of the Kyoto Protocol was to work out the scale and speed of emission cuts needed globally to hit a certain global warming target, and then for countries to negotiate how to divide up those cuts between them. By contrast, under the Paris Agreement, each country makes its own unilateral commitment to reduce emissions; if cumulatively these commitments are not enough to reach the temperature target (and currently they are not), governments are supposed to progressively strengthen

Whatever your view, there is no doubt that in the immediate aftermath of the summit, Copenhagen felt very much like a failure. Governments had promised to deliver a new comprehensive global agreement in line with science. Instead, in the dismal snowbound pit of Copenhagen's Bella Centre, the formal negotiations foundered in a stinking miasma of diplomatic maladroitness and mutual mistrust, and governments agreed nothing more than a short political declaration of dubious legitimacy and low ambition. Obama failed his first big test of global leadership, Europe vacillated, the BASICs bloc sat on their fellow developing countries – and it appeared unlikely, at that point, that presidents and prime ministers would ever want to try anything similar again.

Whether the fuss over the hacked emails and the Himalayan glaciers contributed to the summit's failure is not certain. Saudi Arabia's lead negotiator told me before the summit that the emails undermined the case for cutting emissions;[36] but no other delegation openly referred to it. In the analysis article I wrote for the BBC immediately afterwards, neither 'Gate' featured on my list of 'eight reasons why Copenhagen failed'.[37]

Even so, the possibility that these episodes made some unenthusiastic delegations even less enthusiastic cannot be discounted – nor is it known how much play business lobbies such as Japan's Keidanren made of them while talking to their ministers.

---

them over time on a cycle of five-yearly reviews. The approach of unilateral pledges emerged at the end of the 2009 summit, in the Copenhagen Accord.

Whatever the answer to that question, there is no doubt that contrarians now had a full armoury. The apparent slowdown in warming at the Earth's surface showed, they said, that climate change would not be as bad as predicted by 'alarmist' scientists. The hacked emails showed that scientists knew this and had conspired to hide the evidence. The Copenhagen debacle proved that governments did not believe climate change to be that serious and would never make a comprehensive global agreement. It would be opposed especially by emerging economies such as China and India, which would continue building coal-fired power stations and consuming ever more oil. And to come full circle – why should they not, given that climate change was obviously not such a serious issue and the science was so questionable?

In a nutshell, this is how we arrived, at the beginning of 2010, at a situation in which the twin narratives on climate change – the 'official' one maintained by scientists and governments, and the 'guerilla' one where science and politics lay broken – could exist side by side.

There is no denying that at the time, some of the sceptics' arguments had weight. Governments *had* collectively failed to do in Copenhagen what they had promised in Bali, and the very existence of the United Nations climate convention as a politically heavyweight entity seemed to hang by a thread. Presidents and prime ministers like to be associated with successes, not failures; and the surreal conclusion to the summit, which saw leaders such as Angela Merkel, Nicolas Sarkozy and Gordon Brown going through the draft Copenhagen Accord line-by-line in an effort to produce something they could hold up as an achievement, was not a scene that any of them would want to risk repeating. China and India (and many other developing nations) were indeed powering ahead with coal. The UK government's chief scientific advisor Sir David King had remarked a few years earlier that China was building one coal-fired power station per week, and he was accurate. Building seemed set to continue, despite the fact that China pledged at Copenhagen to reduce its emissions intensity[j] by 40-45 per cent by 2020.[38]

Solar and wind energy – the two forms of renewable energy with the biggest potential for global expansion – were still markedly more expensive than coal-fired generation, and no country bar Norway saw electric cars as a serious near-term option.[39]

On the climate science side, it appeared that there really had been a slowdown in the rate of surface temperature rise. The graph had risen only slightly since 1998, and scientists did not have a clear explanation. Kevin Trenberth from the US National Center for Atmospheric Research, a lead author on three successive IPCC reports, acknowledged this in one of the hacked emails: 'The fact is that we can't account for the lack of warming at the moment and it is a travesty that we can't.'[40]

Nigel Lawson was not the only contrarian with a book out. In October 2009, journalist and author Christopher Booker published *The Real Global Warming Disaster*.[41] It takes us from the nineteenth

---

[j] The greenhouse gas emissions associated with a unit of GDP

century discovery of the natural greenhouse effect and the gases responsible for it, through the realisation that coal burning could cause global warming, to the first UN conference on the environment in Stockholm in 1972 and on to the approaching Copenhagen Summit.

It is largely framed as a conspiracy story – how a small group of scientists and politicians obsessed with man-made climate change and in some cases with world government invented a scare story and perpetuated it for their own political ends. It details the 'hockey-stick controversy' of the early 2000s, and alleged manipulation of the IPCC by 'warmist' scientists and politicians, with former US Vice-President Al Gore cast as manipulator-in-chief.

Events unfolding now at the University of East Anglia and with the IPCC's Himalayas fail appeared, in some circles, to prove his thesis correct, with the collapse of the Copenhagen talks the evidence that 'warmists' had been rumbled.

Of course, there was all along – if I may borrow a favourite contrarian phrase – 'another side to the story'. To all of these points there were counters. Certainly, computer models of the climate system had not foreseen the slowdown – but then they were not designed to predict relatively short-term events. And even though scientists were struggling to find the correct explanation for the slowdown, several plausible ones existed, including a cooling effect from natural cycles in the ocean and increasing output of cooling soot from China's coal-fired power stations.[42,43]

And if there really had been a slowdown, it was a story with two very different possible endings. In the sceptics' version, it meant that climate change would not be as serious as mainstream science had forecast. In the other version, what it meant was that some factor had been masking temperature rise for a decade; if and when that factor went away, global warming would probably accelerate with a vengeance. If the second version proved correct but the political world allowed itself to be lulled by the first into taking its collective foot off the pedal of decarbonisation, a serious shock lay ahead.

In any case, it was plain to see that the year which contrarians selected as the start of the slowdown – 1998 – had seen abnormally high temperatures because of strong El Niño conditions; so of course, succeeding years were likely to be cooler. No-one had ever predicted a smooth, even rising of the global temperature with no blips on it. And the 1998 El Niño was a pretty big blip. On the economics of energy, the 'other side of the story' was less tangible. But some governments (mainly in Europe, including the UK) were investing in renewable energy, and it was reasonable to suppose that in time, this would bring costs down for everyone. In China, air pollution was emerging as a significant public concern, and it could not be tackled without reducing coal use. And if the world was to head in a clean energy direction, then China would want to do most of the manufacturing.

The international politics looked more murky. But from the ashes of Copenhagen, a new international grouping of countries had arisen, the Cartagena Dialogue, preparing to raise the phoenix of a new global settlement. And there was always the prospect of Barack Obama making climate change his signature issue once he had reformed US healthcare – which, eventually, he did.

So: the battle-lines were set. Twin visions of climate change and energy: facts, claims, spin, reputations, repudiations. The next 10 years would determine who was right.

2

The evidence arrives

Across the vast mass of contrarian writings, you will find a number of different arguments displayed against acting to reduce greenhouse gas emissions. There are different ways to cut the arguments cake, but I have chosen to slice it into eight segments, running from simple denial that the climate is changing to contentions over economics and geopolitics. Contrarians to this day cleave to various mixtures of these arguments, and you can find many of them laid out clearly on the pages of *An Appeal to Reason*.

I have tried to keep these eight sections short. But in some cases I have failed, because doing justice to the reasons why contrarian arguments have turned out to be wrong sometimes involves diving down rabbit holes of science and economics, returning to the surface trailing copious bundles of jargon. If you are already familiar with climate science, energy economics or the geopolitics of these issues you may want to skip some or even all of the sections. I have included a short bullet-pointed summary at the beginning of each section in case the rabbit-holes look too murky.

a. *The climate isn't changing*

Rhetoric:

'The world is getting colder and polar bears are not drowning... one day we may look back with amazement on our panic over global warming'
– Daily Express leader, Nov 2009.[44]

Reality:

- Multiple records show the Earth's average global temperature has increased by about 1°C since the Industrial Revolution, with the bulk of that warming occurring since the 1970s
- Other signs of a changing climate abound, such as shrinking of mountain glaciers and polar ice, sea-level rise and animal migration
- Ocean water is becoming less alkaline (more acidic) as it absorbs CO_2.

There is so much evidence that the Earth is warming that I was tempted to make this a one-word section: 'Really??'

But it is an argument that you still come across, if not any longer from most leading contrarians. So I had better treat it seriously.

As the saying goes in Melbourne: 'If you don't like the weather – wait a minute'. The weather is always changing, from day to day and from year to year; and presumably that will continue whatever climatic future we create for ourselves.

Even Venus and Jupiter, with climates very different from ours, have weather. Just as on Earth, it involves hugely complex interactions of winds, cloud formation – and on Earth, ocean currents – which are driven fundamentally by uneven distribution of heat across the planet.

While many aspects of weather are random, some have a pattern. Natural cycles exist that have a warming or cooling effect, transferring heat from ocean to atmosphere in one phase, vice-versa in the opposite phase. The best known of these is the El Niño Southern Oscillation (ENSO) where cycles last 3-8 years.[45] There are others in the Pacific and Atlantic oceans in which cooling and warming phases last for decades.[46,47]

So, attempting to track changes in the global temperature by looking at a sequence of individual years is fraught with difficulties, because the signal being looked for – a progressive warming or cooling – can be drowned out by these natural cycles and by random changes.

Because of the length of some natural cycles, scientists conventionally refer to 'the climate' as the set of conditions over a period of 30 years.[48] A description of 'the climate' at any time will include information about the average values for each parameter – temperature, rainfall, storminess, and so on – as well as how they vary day-to-day and year-to-year. 'Climate change', then, is a change that can be seen over a timescale of several decades. As the IPCC puts it:

> 'Climate change refers to a change in the state of the climate that can be identified (e.g., by using statistical tests) by changes in the mean and/or the variability of its properties, and that persists for an extended period, typically decades or longer. [49]

So – on that definition, is the climate changing? Unequivocally, yes.

The simplest way of demonstrating that change is to look at the graph of the global average temperature since the late ninteenth century, when the Industrial Revolution was getting into full swing. There are basically two phases of distinct warming – one running from the turn of the century through to about 1940, the other from about 1970 and still continuing, with a plateau in between. There are minor bumps and jumps along the way, caused by El Niño periods, La Niña periods, volcanic eruptions (which cool the Earth for a few years), and – well – weather. But the overall pattern is clear.

And this is not the finding of a single research group. The UK's HadCRUT record, those maintained by the American government agencies NOAA[50] and NASA[51], by the Japan Meteorological Agency[52], by the independent Berkeley Earth Project[53] – all show the same basic pattern. They vary in the details because they use different methods of collating and analysing data – but the basic trend is unarguable.

But the global average temperature at the Earth's surface is by no means the only manifestation of climate change. A 'changing climate' also involves regional changes which in some cases will be far more visible than the global trend. It implies changes to rains and winds, to the frequency and duration of droughts and storms. It may involve changes to ocean currents, and may perturb natural events that seem imperturbable, such as the Gulf Stream or the Asian monsoon.

Are scientists detecting those changes?

Unequivocally, yes; not everywhere and not on every count, but on many counts in many regions.[54] In some places, such as the Arctic, the surface temperature is warming faster than the global average. Logically, that means that some regions show slower warming than the global average – the southern US is one.[55] Warming is faster over land than the ocean, and faster in the Northern Hemisphere than the Southern.

In virtually every inhabited part of the world, people are experiencing a greater number of hot days and a lower number of cold days than 50 years ago. Winter snow is progressively changing to rain in North America, northern Japan and the Alps. Europe and parts of Asia are seeing more frequent heatwaves. In the Mediterranean and West Africa, droughts are becoming more frequent. In North America, extreme rainfall events have become more common.

In some regions such as Africa and Antarctica it is not yet possible to determine trends due to a lack of reliable weather station records.

The physical world is giving us many other signals of a changing climate. In the Arctic, the ice floes that cover the ocean are covering less and less of it in summertime,[56] a trend happening so quickly that scientists sometimes refer to the 'Arctic sea ice death spiral'.[57] There is considerable variation between individual years – but the overall trend is clear, so much so that in a few decades' time there will probably be virtually no Arctic sea ice at all in summer. The giant ice sheet that covers Greenland is losing ice to the sea.[58]

The Antarctic is very different from the Arctic – whereas the Arctic is basically ocean surrounded by land, the Antarctic is land surrounded by ocean. The continent of Antarctica is so big and so cold that its weather system is to some extent isolated from global trends. The majority of the ice lies in the east of the continent – and this seems to be largely unaffected by temperature rise. The same is not true of West Antarctica. Here, like Greenland, the ice sheet is unequivocally losing ice to the sea.[59]

Across the globe, mountain glaciers show a marked decline. Some are increasing in length and thickness, but most are getting thinner and shorter. Of 166 glaciers routinely surveyed around the world, more than 80 per cent are losing mass.[60] Both the proportion of glaciers losing mass and the total ice mass being lost each year are increasing.

Then there is sea level rise. It has two main causes – one is simply that water expands as it gets warmer, the other is that when ice on land melts, it eventually finds its way into the ocean. Sea level rise is measured by instruments on the shore and by satellites. There are regional variations, and there are places where the sea level is falling relative to the land. But there is no doubt that globally, it is rising.[61]

As the independent scientist James Lovelock once told me, sea-level rise is a much better indicator of long-term change than surface temperature because it is relatively undisturbed by all of the natural cycles and weather variations that put kinks into the surface temperature graph.

The ocean is heating up. The top layers are getting warmer about half as quickly as the Earth's surface; deeper, it is a slower process.[62] Observation has become much more systematic since the year 2000 with the deployment of several thousand semi-autonomous

ARGO floats across the global ocean.[63]

Two other profound changes are taking place in the ocean. One is a change in the pH of seawater from alkaline towards acid, caused by the absorption of carbon dioxide from the atmosphere.[64] The other, much more recently identified, is a reduction in the oxygen content of seawater.

Finally, there is nature. Around the world, hundreds, perhaps thousands of species of plants and animals have been recorded doing things associated with springtime – budding, breeding, flowering, coming out of hibernation – earlier in the year than they used to.[65] In the UK alone, hundreds of species show such trends.[66,67]

Many species are moving, either away from the Equator towards the North or South Pole or uphill, so as to stay in the range of temperatures for which they have evolved.[68] The average speed of migration, across hundreds of species studied, has been estimated at 17km per decade on land, and twice as fast in the ocean.[69,70] For plankton – which sit at the base of the ocean food web – the rate of movement is enormous, hundreds of kilometres per decade.

For anyone who looks at the science, it is really hard, now, to argue that the world's climate is not changing. Most contrarians do not even try. The only ways to prolong the life of this canard are to ignore the evidence or to proclaim that the entirety of climate science is bent. More of that later.

b. <u>*The climate is changing, but it always has done, and it's all natural*</u>

Rhetoric:

'The erroneous assumption that the dominant driving force for global warming is the emission of CO_2 by humans has been made without considering the effects of the sun, tectonics, earth's orbital oscillations, oceanic oscillations or extra-terrestrial radiation' – *Professor Ian Plimer, The Spectator, 2017*[71]

Reality:

- The climate has changed as far back as we can see in Earth history – but that does not mean that modern climate change is natural too.
- The pace of modern global warming is extraordinarily fast by comparison with the geological record.
- There are 'fingerprints' on modern-day climate change that prove its human origin.

If the argument that modern-day climate change is entirely natural sounds familiar, that could be because you just heard it from someone in the entourage of the leader of the 'free' world. Perhaps from Scott Pruitt, boss of the US Environmental Protection Agency until his scandal-laden departure earlier this year, who wrote in 2016: 'Scientists continue to disagree about the degree and extent of global warming and its connection to the actions of mankind.'[72]

Or maybe from NASA chief Jim Bridenstine, who said during one of his confirmation hearings: 'It's gonna depend on a whole lot of factors... In some years you could say absolutely [greenhouse gases are the most important factor]. In other years during sun cycles and other things there are other contributing factors that would maybe have more than an impact.'[73,74]

The argument is attractive because it is a part-truism: the climate *has* always changed, and would continue doing so if *Homo sapiens* had never evolved. But the historical existence of natural climate change is also an irrelevant argument – logically, it cannot be used to prove that current climate change is natural too. More importantly, no natural processes have been identified on Earth or beyond that can explain what is happening now. And there are specific 'fingerprints' that show we have an artificial rather than a natural process at work.

The first aspect of current climate change that marks it out as something different is its speed.

For the last 800,000 years, the Earth has been in a cycle of Ice Ages and warmer 'interglacial' periods. The cause is well-known – slight changes in the Earth's orbit around the sun, causing small variations in solar energy reaching Earth whose effects are amplified by processes such as melting of ice and freezing of water – known as Milankovitch Cycles after the Serbian scientist who identified them.[75]

The temperature difference between Ice Age and interglacial is about 5°C, and the transition between them takes at least 5,000 years – a rate of warming of about 1°C per thousand years.[76] Now, by contrast, the climate has warmed by about 1°C in the course of 100 years.[77] So, the current observed rate of global warming is about 10 times faster than those natural transitions.

The contrast is actually more acute, because the majority of the 1°C rise has occurred since the 1970s; using this figure, the current warming rate is at least 20 times faster. Ocean acidity is changing even faster – about 50 times faster than at any time identified in the Earth's history.[78]

Modern-day global warming is fast even by comparison with the occasional gargantuan upheavals that literally re-shaped the face of the Earth. About 250 million years ago the Earth went through one of the so-called 'Great Extinction' events, which marks the boundary between the geological Permian and Triassic periods.[79] Vast quantities of molten basalt rock spewed from the Earth's mantle onto the surface in what is now Siberia. The eruption liberated carbon dioxide into the atmosphere, and the planet warmed for 800,000 years. Even here the rate of warming was tiny compared with today's – 1°C per 50,000 years.[80]

Coming up into more recent history, you will often hear the argument that current climate change cannot be considered exceptional because the Earth was 'warmer than today in mediaeval times' or 'warmer just after the last Ice Age'. To give those claims their scientific terms, the argument is for a Mediaeval Warm Period about 1,050-750 years ago, and a Holocene Climate Optimum 9,000-5,000 years ago, both warmer than today.[k]

The real story is slightly more complex. Its telling has been hampered by the fact that these periods lie a

---

[k] The Holocene is the current interglacial period, from the end of the last Ice Age onwards

long time before the age of thermometers. The data is stored in numerous 'proxy' records – the growth rings of trees and stalactites, the concentration of tiny marine animals' shells in ocean sediment, the ratios of different chemical elements' isotopes. Temperature has to be inferred, not measured directly. These analyses were undertaken first in Europe and North America, meaning that a regional story emerged before the global one. And that regional one, with its tales of 'Vikings growing grapes in Greenland',[81] turns out to be unrepresentative of the Earth as a whole.

The most comprehensive analysis of the last 2,000 years brings together records from all seven continents. It shows that temperatures in each region of the Earth varied differently.[82] It is impossible to define a global Mediaeval Warm Period, the scientists concluded; and over the last 1,400 years, the global average temperature today was never as high as it is now.

A similar reconstruction of proxy data going back 11,300 years to the end of the last Ice Age gives a comprehensive picture of the Holocene Climate Optimum.[83] The scientists concluded that the Earth saw '~0.6°C of warming from the early Holocene (11,300 yr before the present day, BP) to a temperature plateau extending from 9,500 to 5,500 yr BP', followed by a cooling from 5,500 onwards.

There are four important takeaways:

1) The temperature may have been slightly higher at the Holocene Climate Optimum than nowadays
2) Both studies confirm that the historical rate of warming was small compared with modern times
3) The second study was able to show that the driver of

warming about 10,000 years ago was a continuation of the Milankovitch cycle

4) However... that study was published in 2013, since when we have had the three warmest years on record. So unless we suddenly enter a period of major global cooling in the next year or two, you can go back to the top of this list and scrap Point One.

For well over a century, scientists have known that humanity's emissions of greenhouse gases would be sufficient to change the climate quickly and significantly. The Swedish academic Svante Arrhenius was the first to calculate the likely impact of rising carbon dioxide (known then as 'carbonic acid').[84,1] With remarkable prescience, he wrote in 1896:

> 'We yet recognise that the slight percentage of carbonic acid in the atmosphere may by the advances of industry be changed to a noticeable degree in the course of a few centuries... any doubling of the percentage of carbon dioxide in the air would raise the temperature of the Earth's surface by 4°C; and if the carbon dioxide were increased fourfold, the temperature would rise by 8°C.'

Nevertheless – despite the extraordinary speed of modern-day climate change, and despite the amply-proven capacity of greenhouse gas emissions to change the Earth's climate in the way that we are seeing now,

---

[1] CO_2 becomes carbonic acid when dissolved in water

there could in principle be a different cause. We could be living, by pure coincidence, in a time when we have put enough greenhouse gases into the atmosphere to produce the changes we are observing in the world around us – but when something else is happening that is the real cause, or at least a large part of the cause. In which case the scientific question is: 'what?'

It is not a question that scientists have been chary of addressing. The obvious thing to look at first is the sun; could changes in its output be enough to drive the rise in global surface temperature and all the other facets of climate change?

The sun's output varies over an 11-year cycle, which clearly could not be driving a temperature rise that has lasted for many decades. It also waxes and wanes over much longer periods. Across the 11-year cycle, and over longer periods, its energy output varies by about 0.1 per cent – enough to change the Earth's temperature by about 0.1°C at most, just one-tenth of the change we have seen over the last century.[85]

The scientist's next question, then, is: 'could there be something happening that is amplifying the effect of this insignificant change?'

Two ideas have been put forward. One hinges on the fact that the sun's output varies by much more in the ultraviolet than for visible light – by up to 10 per cent. In the atmosphere, ultraviolet radiation produces ozone – a greenhouse gas. Could more ultraviolet radiation be producing more ozone, causing what you might term 'natural' greenhouse gas warming?

The second theory concerns cosmic rays – very fast-moving particles from deep space that collide with gas molecules in the atmosphere. This creates electrically-charged particles which could help clouds to form. When the sun's output is 'weak', so is the solar wind, a protective bubble of charged particles given off by the sun. When the solar wind is weak, more cosmic rays penetrate to the Earth's atmosphere, creating more clouds. And the density of clouds in the atmosphere could change the Earth's temperature. This idea has been around since 1959 but came to prominence in 2007 in a book, *The Chilling Stars*, co-written by Danish physicist Henrik Svensmark.[86] It also featured heavily in *The Great Global Warming Swindle*, a polemical film screened by Channel Four the same year.[87]

They are both interesting ideas. But neither is driving modern-day climate change.

It turns out that the ultraviolet mechanism can at most produce a global temperature difference of about 0.2°C.[88]

For the cosmic ray theory to work, several links in the chain have to be demonstrated: cosmic rays have to create more charged particles during a period of 'weak' sun, those charged particles have to lead to formation of more clouds, and the clouds have to have a sufficiently large cooling effect. Science has probed each of these links in the chain of causality... and has disproved them all. Production of charged particles does not increase across a solar cycle,[89] and there is no link between the strength of cosmic rays and cloudiness.[90]

The real clincher though, for any proposed mechanism by which the sun is supposed to be driving modern-day climate change, is that since about 1980, the sun's output has declined, delivering a net cooling effect to the Earth. In the same period, the Earth's surface has warmed by about half a degree Celsius.[91,92] Whatever is causing modern-day climate change, it is clearly not the sun.

Another 'natural' theory that has been proposed, tested and discarded is that all of the observed warming can be explained by the Pacific Multidecadal Oscillation (PDO). Proposed by Dr Roy Spencer, a NASA-affiliated scientist whose day job is producing one of the records of global temperature derived from satellites rather than weather stations, this theory holds that the 'phase' of the PDO – whether the ocean is transferring heat to the atmosphere or the other way round – affects cloud formation around the world enough to change the planet's surface temperature by about 0.5°C.[93]

This also turns out not to be correct. Scientists have looked both at the PDO and its Atlantic cousin, the AMO – and found that while they do have an impact on global temperatures, it is significantly outweighed by the influence of greenhouse gas emissions.[94] The ocean cycles are responsible for perhaps 10 per cent, no more, of warming over the last half-century.[95] In any case, it is obvious that their influence will be cyclical – what goes up will eventually come down.

Often the IPCC is accused of neglecting anything other than greenhouse gases in its assessment reports. This is simply incorrect: the merest glance at its 2013 report, for example, turns up a chapter explicitly titled 'Anthropogenic and Natural Radiative Forcing'.[96] The factors that it analyses include:

- carbon dioxide from fossil fuel burning
- other greenhouse gases produced by human

activities, including methane, nitrous oxide and hydrofluorocarbons

- aerosols (tiny dust and soot particles in the atmosphere, from industry and dry land)
- volcanic eruptions
- changes in the sun's energy output, including cosmic rays
- changes in the Earth's albedo (how much incoming solar energy is reflected back into space)
- changes in natural sources and sinks[m] of carbon dioxide, including forests and the ocean
- Milankovitch cycles
- changes to ozone in both the troposphere and stratosphere
- contrails produced by aircraft.

Although greenhouse gas emissions are by some distance the strongest factor, some of the others are also influential – some causing warming, others cooling. Over shorter time periods, natural ocean cycles can also warm or cool. So, the next logical question to ask is: 'how much of the observed global warming is caused by greenhouse gas emissions?'

The answer appears to be: 'since the middle of the century, a bit more than all of it'.

The global temperature rise up to about 1940 appears to have been driven by a mixture of natural factors added to greenhouse gas warming. The two main natural factors were an increase in the sun's

---

[m] A 'sink' is something that absorbs carbon dioxide from the atmosphere, forests being the most obvious example

energy output,[97] and the end to a series of five major planet-cooling volcanic eruptions, from Krakatoa in 1883 to Novarupta in 1912.[98,99]

Then comes a mid-century plateau, whose main cause appears to have been at least partially human-induced, as the re-building of industry after World War 2 increased factories' and power stations' emissions of aerosols, which act like dust from volcanic eruptions to cool the planet. Then warming begins again.

The 2017 US National Climate Assessment calculates that, after accounting for the influence of aerosols and all these other factors, greenhouse gas emissions accounted for 93-123 per cent of the global warming seen since 1950.[100] Other assessments have come to broadly the same conclusion.[101] It is worth mentioning that, since the 1970s, not only has the sun's output weakened, we also had more major volcanic eruptions. So natural influences have been working to cool the planet – while the planet has unequivocally warmed.

Three other pieces of evidence merit mention here. One is that, just as the Earth's surface and lower atmosphere – the troposphere – are warming, the upper atmosphere – the stratosphere – is getting colder.[102] This is exactly what you would expect to happen under greenhouse gas warming: by trapping energy in the troposphere, less escapes into the upper stratosphere, which therefore gets cooler. It is not what you would expect were warming being driven by the sun putting out more energy.

The second is that, when satellites look at the energy being reflected off the Earth's surface and back into space, they detect that energy is being removed at exactly the wavelengths absorbed by molecules of greenhouse gases such as carbon dioxide. And the amount being removed is increasing over time.[103]

The third shows that the additional carbon dioxide in the atmosphere comes from burning fossil fuels rather than from some natural process.

This finding comes from studying the ratios of different isotopes of carbon present in atmospheric CO_2. Carbon in fossil fuels is depleted in both the rarer isotopes, ^{13}C and ^{14}C – and as the CO_2 concentration in the atmosphere increases, the proportion of these isotopes in it is falling, proving that the additional CO_2 came from fossil fuel burning.[104] The amount of CO_2 entering the atmosphere each year also tallies well with evidence on what is being emitted from factories, cars and such like, and what is being absorbed by land and sea.

Science has been clear for more than 150 years that rising concentrations of greenhouse gases will have a warming effect on the Earth, and we have had estimates of the likely scale of that effect for more than 100. In general, observations over the last century tally well with theory. Every other idea so far proposed has failed; and there are specific fingerprints of humanity's greenhouse gas emissions on the warming that we see.

So – insist that modern-day climate change has a 'natural' cause, if you want – but the evidence is completely against you.

c. <u>*It won't be that bad – maybe even good*</u>

Rhetoric:

'Even if the world warms as much as the consensus expects, the net harm still looks small alongside the real harm now being done by preventable causes; and if it does warm this much, it will be because more people are rich enough to afford to do something about it. As usual, optimism gets a bad press in this debate.'
– Matt Ridley, The Rational Optimist

Reality:

- Climate change is already increasing the frequency of extreme weather events
- Claims that 'global warming stopped' and 'computer models exaggerate warming' are not supportable
- Climate science projects a range of risks ahead, from manageable to catastrophic – and the only rational way to approach it is to acknowledge the range of possibilities.

'Climate change will not be so bad' is the clarion call of a school of contrarianism whose proponents style themselves 'lukewarmers'. Its most prominent UK adherent is the hereditary peer and science writer Matt Ridley. His argument is that while the fundamental idea that greenhouse gas emissions warm the planet is correct, the forecasts of mainstream scientists are too alarmist, and what transpires will be less serious than their projections.

A related argument is that for decades to come, the impacts of climate change will be negligible (and in many cases beneficial) – and if climate change ever needs solving, we can do so in later decades when society is richer and perhaps cleverer.

Again, it is an appealing argument, because it is another truism: maybe climate change will not be that bad. After all, every projection that climate scientists make comes with a range of imprecision – inevitable, when you are trying to model the hugely complex climate system with imperfect knowledge. In a situation like this, it is entirely possible to choose to believe the most optimistic number, and to back that up by citing only those scientific studies that back your belief.

Although lukewarmers claim their positions are science-based, they are not. Lukewarmery is as unscientific as contending that the planet is not warming; but for a different reason. Outright denial of climate change depends on ignoring a vast and ever-growing mountain of observational evidence. Lukewarmery hinges on selecting only those bits of evidence that fit your theory, bestowing upon them the accolade of 'the facts', and ignoring or disputing the rest. Rather than evidence-based opinion-forming, the thought process is perhaps best described as opinion-based evidence-selection.

It works whether you are discussing sea level rise, the tipping point for irreversible melting of the Greenland ice sheet, the possible drying out of the Amazon rainforest, or any other manifestation of climate change. But a lot of discourse centres on the key concept of 'climate sensitivity'. Essentially, this is how much warming results from a certain increase in greenhouse gases in the atmosphere. Classically, equilibrium climate sensitivity is defined as the temperature rise eventually resulting from a doubling of the carbon dioxide concentration.[105]

The IPCC's Fifth Assessment Report, having collated all of the various values for climate sensitivity derived from present-day observations, computer models and geological records of Earth history,[106] concluded that the value probably lies in the range 1.5-4.5°C.[107]

While impacts of 1.5°C of global warming would be manageable in some parts of the world, impacts of 4.5°C would not. For context, it is almost the same as the temperature difference between an Ice Age and an interglacial – which comes with a difference of about 120 metres in sea level. So the lack of precision in this one very central measure of climate change is far from ideal. Nevertheless, it is what it is; we cannot demand of science a degree of precision that it cannot deliver.

It is worth mentioning too that a CO_2 rise of 40 per cent has so far brought us global warming of 1°C. So the chances of a 100 per cent rise bringing us global warming of only 1.5°C appear intuitively small. This is not strictly speaking a scientific observation as we are talking about one point in time rather than an extended equilibrium period; but still, as Nigel Lawson has himself observed, measurements are not unimportant.

If you identify yourself as a lukewarmer, the obvious approach is to highlight scientific papers that come up with a low estimate of climate sensitivity and ignore or criticise those that produce higher numbers. This is exemplified by Matt Ridley, who – for example – promoted a recent scientific paper[108] concluding that climate sensitivity lies at the lower end of the IPCC's estimates (1.2–3.1°C)[109,110], but chose not to highlight another paper emerging two months later suggesting the opposite (estimate 2.4-4.6°C).[111]

To be fair to Ridley, he acknowledges that he endorses papers that he finds 'persuasive' and which back his pre-existing beliefs.[112] Well; there is probably not a person anywhere in the world completely immune to confirmation bias. But it is not science.

The only approach that is scientifically sound – and the only feasible one for policymakers – is to acknowledge the entirety of the evidence, which equates to a range of risks ahead.

Of recurring interest in lukewarmist circles is the idea that computer models of the climate system 'run too hot' – in other words, they are programmed to over-estimate the likely course of climate change. The idea originated in the years leading up to 2008, and it was then a reasonable claim to make, given that the global surface temperature rise appeared to have slowed, unpredicted by climate models.

Whether there was actually a 'global warming slowdown is a complex question. One problem is that the average temperature across the Earth's surface cannot be measured with absolute precision; we do not have weather stations everywhere. Within the limitations imposed by this imprecision, the IPCC report in 2013 concluded it was possible that there had been no slowdown at all, and equally possible that there had been a small decline; most likely, the global surface temperature continued rising, but at about one-third of the speed seen in the decades before 1998.[113]

Of the world's three major established surface temperature records, the one in which the slowdown showed up most clearly was the UK's HadCRUT. Scientists maintaining the record had acknowledged for years that it suffers from incomplete data coverage in Africa and the Polar regions. And yet these regions are warming faster than the global average. So, whether HadCRUT adequately represented the global picture was an openly-discussed question.

In 2013, British chemist Kevin Cowtan and Canadian geographer Robert Way – scientists who approached the issue with fresh minds, as neither had a background in climate change – produced a revised version of the HadCRUT record in which they used temperature readings from satellites to fill in the missing bits.[114] They were able to show that this produced a more accurate temperature record than the HadCRUT original. What it did not show was a pause or even a slowdown in surface warming.

More recently still, in 2015 scientists from the US National Oceanic and Atmospheric Administration (NOAA) re-analysed and updated their surface temperature record. They added data from more years and more weather stations, and corrected for errors in historical measurements of sea surface temperature. Their conclusion, also, was that there never was a pause in surface warming.[115]

Only about one per cent of the extra energy being trapped by the Earth's enhanced greenhouse gas blanket is stored in the atmosphere. By contrast, an estimated 93 per cent goes into the ocean.[116] And when scientists asked whether there was a 'global warming pause' that included a hiatus in ocean warming, the answer was definitively 'no'.[117,118]

These findings have more or less put paid to the idea that there was a global warming pause. There is also the wider point that none of the other manifestations of climate change – the disappearance of Arctic summer sea ice, the melting of glaciers across the world, the migration of animals – underwent a hiatus. Not everyone agrees – the UK Met Office, for example, continues to talk about the existence of a former pause in the directly observed surface temperature. But last year it too declared that the pause was definitively over, as 2014, 2015 and 2016 successively broke the record for the warmest year on record.[119]

The 'pause' narrative was constructed largely through cherry-picking the year when it was supposed to have started. 1998 was exceptionally hot, driven by one of the strongest El Niño events on record, which pushed up the global surface temperature by about 0.1-0.2°C.[120] Logic tells you that after an exceptionally hot year, the following years are likely to be cooler, even if there is an underlying upwards trend.[121]

El Niño also played a role in lifting temperatures in 2015 and 2016. An early estimate suggests its effect was also around 0.2°C.[122]

Perhaps the biggest irony is that having started the pause narrative by highlighting the relatively slow years after El Niño-fuelled 1998, some contrarians claimed the 2014-16 records were not real because they had been stoked by – er – El Niño conditions.

However: the reality is that there is a big temperature difference between 1998 and 2016. It is probaably about 0.25°C, and perhaps as much as 0.4°C.[123,124] This is down to global warming – the progressive temperature rise, primarily driven by greenhouse gas emissions, on top of which the El Niño temperature spikes sit. Indeed, the World Meteorological Organisation has plotted a graph that divides years into those that saw an El Niño, those with the opposing La Niña condition, and those with neither.[125] For all three categories, the upwards trend is clearly visible.

Coming bang up to date: during 2017, the Pacific Ocean moved out of its El Niño phase and towards cooling La Niña conditions. And yet 2017 ended up as the second or third warmest year on record.[126] 2018 looks set to be the fourth warmest even if El Niño conditions do not develop at the end of the year, which appears possible.

The end to the idea of a 'global warming slowdown' has also put paid to any notion that there is a systematic 'warm' bias in computer models.

Models have evolved a huge amount in recent years, taking account of more and more processes in the Earth system. One recent analysis assessed the performance of eight generations of model dating back to 1975, and compared their forecasts of the rate of surface warming for the period 1970-2016 with the observed rate.[127] In chronological sequence, the models turn out to have over- or under-estimated the rate of warming by +30%, -20%, +30%, +17%, -28%, -14%, +8% and +16%; from which one can deduce that they have not performed perfectly, but there is no systematic 'warm' bias.

The last five generations of model are those used in the five assessment reports that the IPCC has published to date. For all of them, the temperatures that we have actually seen lie within the ranges projected by the models; occasionally a year may lie outside the range, but these will be the unusually cold or warm years driven by El Niño or La Niña events which are hard to predict more than a few months ahead.

Professor Judith Curry wrote a short report in 2017 for GWPF highlighting issues that she finds with computer models; the main graph in her report too shows the observed global temperature record generally lying within the range of model forecasts.[128]

To summarise: if there ever was a slowdown in global surface temperature rise, it is long gone. Computer models are not systematically over-estimating the rate of global warming. On the sensitivity of the climate system to carbon dioxide levels, studies come up with a significant range of values; and the only valid approach, scientifically and for policymaking, is to acknowledge that the range is large, not to select various values as being true on the basis of pre-existing beliefs.

There is one more specific manifestation of lukewarmery that needs attention: economics. Nigel Lawson's intellectual reputation rests in this field, thus it is no surprise that it finds a prominent place in *An Appeal to Reason*.

For Lawson, the argument that 'climate change won't be so bad' rests largely on a simple economic comparison. He begins with the 'scenarios' that the IPCC used in its 2007 Fourth Assessment Report to contemplate the economic future of human society and thus the likely progression of carbon emissions.[129] These scenarios are possibilities, not forecasts; the point of the IPCC's exercise was to provide policymakers with indications of how various policy choices might affect the progression of climate change and the future costs of addressing it.

Taking one of these scenarios and applying his own assumptions about how economic growth will be split between developed and developing nations, Lawson calculates that in the presence of climate change '...our great-grandchildren in the developed world would, in a hundred years' time, be only 2.6 times as well off as we are today, instead of 2.7 times [in the absence of climate change], and their counterparts in the developing world would be 'only' 8.5 times as well off as people in the developing world are today instead of 9.5 times as well off.'[130]

The argument he makes is that climate change cannot be such a serious threat if all it does is to trim the extent of economic growth by these numbers.

Lawson's calculations may in and of themselves be correct. But they cannot give a meaningful picture of the seriousness, or lack of it, of climate change, whose most important impacts lie well beyond the subtraction of a couple of percentage points from GDP output. For example, even at 1.5°C of global warming, 70-90 per cent of coral reefs in the tropics are forecast to suffer severe damage from climate change and ocean acidification.[131] This potentially means losing the majority of their species, turning them from rich vibrant ecosystems either to barren ocean floor or dull monocultures of those few corals that can survive in a warming and acidifying ocean which is also hit by pollution, invasive species, disease and destructive fishing. You can put a monetary figure on the value of those reefs – economists have done so, and for peoples who rely on fishing and tourism, the economic impacts may be severe – but it is surely missing the point. It is as futile as trying to put an economic value on jazz or love.

Even if you would like to base climate change policy

purely on economics, the reality is that the economists leading the IPCC's analysis cannot produce accurate costings of impacts. This is not my view, but their own. In the Fourth Assessment Report – the one to which Lawson refers in *An Appeal To Reason* – they spell out the limitations.[132]

Costs and benefits of climate impacts on society are 'difficult to estimate', they write. Studies of the macroeconomic costs of climate change are few, and 'generalising from scattered cases that are not necessarily representative of the global portfolio of situations is risky'. 'Many types of costs – especially to society – are poorly captured by monetary metrics.'

Things were no better when the IPCC performed its fifth global assessment, in 2013-14.[133] Economic impacts from climate change are 'difficult to estimate,' it reads. Estimates 'depend on a large number of assumptions, many of which are disputable'. Many 'do not account for catastrophic changes, tipping points, and many other factors.' For a *coup de grace*, it concludes that estimates of the incremental cost of emitting a tonne of carbon, via the damage it does, 'lie between a few dollars and several hundreds of dollars'.

Wait – what?

As anyone who follows the process knows, the IPCC assesses the quality of evidence as well as the conclusions towards which that evidence points. This is a vital component of all science – just think about the difference between planning a rocket mission to land on Mars if you are certain about the nature of the Martian surface, versus doing so when you are uncertain whether it is bog or basalt.

Assessing the quality of evidence ought also to be a

vital ingredient of politics. If as Prime Minister you are contemplating invading a Middle Eastern country on the basis that it possesses weapons of mass destruction, you would surely want to know that your information was of the highest quality before committing to an act that would cost many thousands of lives, incur a huge financial cost and potentially produce decades of instability in the region – would you not?

In short – Lord Lawson bestows on the IPCC's estimates of climate change economics a degree of confidence that their own authors do not pretend exists. His argument that climate change won't be that bad, based on this single part of the IPCC's assessment of impact costs, is thus impossible to justify.

In his book, Lawson's language appeals not only to reason but also to emotion. A constant feature is the use of innocuous, even positive words to describe the extent of global warming thus far – 'modest', 'small', and 'gentle'. Who could fail to approve, as the cold winds of winter swirl around the House of Lords, of a little 'gentle warming'?

This emotional appeal rests on three important fallacies. One is the implicit assumption that what is gentle for the UK is gentle for everyone and everything else. As I have shown, compared against the Earth's great natural climate cycles, the current speed of warming and ocean acidification is extraordinarily high. In terms of its impact on nature, 'brutal' would not be an unreasonable word to use.

If we prefer to focus on people, then it is worth reflecting, among many other examples, that in parts of Africa and South Asia subsistence farmers are already growing crops in conditions that are on the edge of feasibility. Coastal communities across the world face an escalating risk of flooding and salt intrusion into groundwater supplies. Try asking the poor of Cape Town how gentle they find the climate change which, according to a recent analysis, made the recent near-catastrophic drought three times more likely to occur.[134]

The claim of 'gentle' climate change falls down a second time by tacitly assuming that the future will be a simple extrapolation of the past – for example, that the increase in impacts seen between one and two degrees Celsius of warming will be comparable to the increase between nought and one. And that is not sustained by science or economics. One example of that is that tipping points are more likely to be crossed between one and two degrees than between zero and one – including significant ones such as triggering unstoppable melting of the Greenland ice sheet, which would eventually raise sea levels by an estimated seven metres.[135]

The third problem is Lawson's use of the 'gentleness' of climate change impacts to date as a reason for not cutting emissions. It is a failing because further climate change is already 'baked in'. It takes time for the climate system to stabilise in response to rising greenhouse gas concentrations; so climate change would continue escalating even if we could magically turn off the carbon tap tomorrow. According to one recent analysis, even in this vanishingly unlikely scenario, global warming could progress far enough to exceed the 1.5°C target that governments agreed at the Paris Summit.[136] So the decision is not 'what is the right course of action given that we have seen 1°C of global warming already?', but 'what is the right course given we may already be committed to 1.5°C of global warming?'

A more realistic definition of warming 'baked in', though, has to take account not just of emissions to date, but also of those that are inevitably going to occur given the power stations, internal combustion engines and industrial plants that already exist. They will not be turned off tomorrow or even the next day; and without a fairly swift systemic change, their emissions will, even if the lukewarmers are right, lock us into rates and levels of climate change unknown in human history.

Now, the only way to construct the case that 'it won't be that bad' is to cherry-pick those parts of the science that you like and reject the rest. But this is the opposite of science itself. 'The science' really has to mean 'all of the science' – no ifs, no buts, no cherries.

d. *We should just adapt to climate change, not try to stop it*

Rhetoric:

'Essentially, adaptation will enable us, if and when it is necessary, greatly to reduce the adverse consequences of global warming, at far less cost than mitigation, to the point where for the world as a whole, these are unlikely greatly to outweigh (if indeed they outweigh at all) the customarily overlooked benefits of global warming.' – *Nigel Lawson, An Appeal to Reason*

Reality:

- Climate adaptation is indeed necessary and already happening
- Some climate impacts cannot be adapted to – and the number of them is likely to increase as climate change progresses further
- The 'adaptation-only' argument originates in political and economic philosophy, not in science

The argument that as a global society we should not try to restrain climate change but instead just adapt to its impacts is one to which Nigel Lawson in particular cleaves. Arguably it forms the central thesis of *An Appeal to Reason*.

The rationale, as set out by Lawson, is a combination of beliefs that 'adaptation will be more cost-effective' and 'nothing else will work'. He assumes that attempts to curb greenhouse gas emissions meaningfully will fail. So adapting to its impacts is the only available strategy, he argues, in addition to being the preferable one economically.

Yet again the argument has some level of appeal because when expressed in normalised terms – 'humans are very adaptable, we always adapt to changing circumstances' – it is another truism. But it obscures some deeper realities.

One is that whereas humans might have tremendous capacity to adapt, it is not infinite; witness the myriad civilisations destroyed by water shortages or diseases to which they could not adapt. Nature's capacity to adapt is also far from infinite, and an 'adaptation only' approach, with no attempt to constrain emissions, would in reality create carnage for nature worldwide.

Also, once the argument that it is impossible to constrain carbon emissions falls – and, as I will show later, it has fallen – there is nothing to force us down the 'adaptation only' path.

The main problem with the argument is that its underlying assumption, that it is possible to adapt to climate change in all its important manifestations, is simply wrong. The most obvious example of an impact that cannot be adapted to is ocean acidification.[137] The ocean currently absorbs about one-quarter of the carbon dioxide that human activities are putting into the atmosphere. Dissolved in seawater, it becomes carbonic acid. Seawater is naturally alkaline, with an average pH of 8.2. As the carbon dioxide concentration in the atmosphere rises, the ocean absorbs more; and the more carbonic acid it contains, the further it will move from the alkaline towards the acidic end of the pH scale.

This is indeed happening, detected by monitoring from coastal stations, buoys and ships in many parts of the ocean.[138] Since the Industrial Revolution, the pH has changed by about 0.1 units, from 8.2 to 8.1, with further change locked in. That may not sound much; but the numbers are much less important than the implications for marine life. Just as birds, mammals, insects and plants have evolved to fit the climatic conditions where they exist, ocean life has evolved to fit a certain set of conditions. Some species can tolerate a huge range of conditions and move quickly from one place to the next; many others cannot. And the speed of change, as I noted earlier, is extraordinary in the context of the Earth's history.

Already, this apparently modest change in pH is

perturbing the ability of various species to sense prey and predators and to reproduce.

One of the earliest impacts was felt by the shellfish-growing industry on the west coast of the US. About a decade ago, three major hatcheries found that the Pacific oysters they were attempting to rear were not forming shells properly. Investigation revealed that the pH of the seawater used in the hatchery had declined to such a level that the carbonate minerals which the growing oysters extract from the water to form their shells were not present in large enough amounts.[139] Further damage occurred over the next few years. In response, Washington State governor Christine Gregoire created an expert commission to identify ways in which government, science and business could respond. Its report contains a lot of ideas for adaptation. Its top recommendation: cut greenhouse gas emissions.[140]

Across the ocean, other impacts of acidification are already being observed. In the Antarctic, tiny creatures called sea butterflies have been found with 'severe levels of shell dissolution'.[141] In several species of fish, larvae show disorientation in acidified waters, being attracted to predators, for example.[142] Projections show that by the end of the century, the drawdown of carbonic acid-rich surface waters to the deep ocean could put the majority of the world's cold-water corals at risk.[143]

Then there is hypoxia, or de-oxygenation. Long predicted by scientists, it has now been shown that tracts of open ocean are becoming depleted in oxygen.[144] This is caused by two factors. One is simply that oxygen is less soluble in warmer water. The other is down to the fact that the top of the ocean warms faster than deeper layers. Warm water rises, cold water sinks; so, as warming progresses, there is less and less mixing between the vertical layers, and less and less oxygen is drawn down into the water column.[145] As fish and most other sea creatures need to take in oxygen from the water, this is obviously a looming problem with unknown consequences.[n] And another to which it might prove rather hard to adapt.

There are examples of species that appear to be coping; but not across the board. Warming water appears to be making fish smaller.[146] Warming and acidification impair hunting for species such as sharks and reproduction for turtles.[147,148] Across the ocean, zones without sufficient oxygen to support fish are expanding.[149] Generally, species are moving polewards, but at varying speeds – hence disrupting symbioses and predator-prey relationships.[150]

As one example of a profound question to which no answer yet exists: every summer, many species of whale migrate to the Arctic Ocean to feed.[151] The best feeding ground is at the edge of the sea ice, where the mixing of cold and warm waters allows copious amounts of plankton to bloom. So; what happens to those whales when there is no sea ice in the Arctic in summer? Will they able to adapt?

---

[n] One could also mention the myriad other issues facing ocean life – plastics, over-fishing, mining of coral reefs, invasive species, coastal pollution – and note that for some species and ecosystems, these threats are synergistic

If no whale biologist knows the answer to that – and none that I have asked does – you can be pretty sure that Lord Lawson does not.

So: projecting the eventual impacts of climate change on the ocean is not simple. A comprehensive analysis would have to include acidification, warming and hypoxia, plus other effects such as disruption of ocean currents, sea-level rise and freshening of surface waters at the poles. Much is unknown, and no scientist would tell you otherwise. But the basic point is surely obvious: the idea that life can adapt, with or without humanity's assistance, across even a fraction of the world's 360 million square kilometres of ocean is just not tenable.

On very limited scales, perhaps we can help ocean life to adapt. One recent study found that creating marine reserves can give some resilience against climate change impacts.[152] But it also concluded: 'Marine reserves will not halt change or stop many of the threats associated with climate change affecting communities within their boundaries'.

Can we adapt to a world in which the global ocean is becoming more damaged and less productive all the time – where coral reefs basically cease to function, where prey and predator are increasingly dislocated in space and time, where the feeding grounds on which entire species rely become barren?

To some extent, we already are doing so. Already, about half of the seafood we eat is farmed rather than hunted.[153] In principle, we can expand this as far as we want to – or just not eat fish. We can use concrete to artificially protect stretches of coast where until now, the natural breakwater of a coral reef has kept the waves dampened down. For our holidays, we can go to see fish in aquaria rather than using a snorkel.

The obvious question, though, is – why would we want to take this path? How is the world better off in this future than in one where humanity has constrained climate change, and so kept the ocean as alive and healthy as possible?

I have highlighted the ocean because it presents the most glaringly obvious example of why the 'we should just adapt to climate change' argument is not viable. But there are others. Examples where there is clearly not infinite capacity to adapt include:

- Climate change-enhanced drought in areas where there are no realistic options for water supply other than rain
- Sea-level rise in low-lying small island nations, where a sufficient degree and regularity of inundation compromises the freshwater supply and may even force abandonment of the nation
- Countries dependent on crops that may increasingly be disrupted by storms.

It is likely, too, that the number of situations where adaptation is impossible will increase as climate change progresses. A subsistence farmer may be able to adjust to increasing drought to a certain extent, but there will come a limit at which crops simply cannot be grown. Bangkok may remain inhabitable if the sea level rises by half a metre; much less so at two metres.

And the situation for nature on land exactly parallels that in the ocean – with the added complication that species migration in response to warming is more likely to be compromised by barriers, either natural (for example, the wrong type of soil) or constructed (such as farmland or cities).

In *An Appeal to Reason*, Lord Lawson cites another argument for an 'adaptation only' strategy – that adaptation will work out cheaper than mitigation (the formal term for 'curbing the extent of climate change'). He does not give estimates for either the cost of decarbonisation or of adaptation – on the former, noting in fact that 'The only honest answer [to the question of how much it would cost to decarbonise our economies] is that we do not know'.[154] However, he does assert that 'the superior cost-effectiveness of adaptation is clear.'[155]

In reality, it is a difficult comparison to make, because adaptation and mitigation are very different in philosophical terms. Adaptation can reduce the impact of a given manifestation of climate change – mitigation reduces the scale of the manifestation itself. Adaptation tends to work locally – building schools on stilts to avoid flooding, changing crop varieties, and so on – whereas the effect of any nation reducing its greenhouse gas emissions will in principle be felt globally.

They also work on different timescales – adaptation measures take effect immediately, whereas the effect of reducing greenhouse gas emissions is felt most strongly several decades ahead. In addition, the economic estimates of both adaptation and mitigation, on a global scale, are subject to exactly the same limitations of modelling imprecision that I mentioned in the last section. So, a cost comparison is not easy.

In any case they are not really 'either-or' options.

For example, there are plenty of economic estimates of climate damages up to 2°C of warming, from which one can in principle calculate the economic benefit of adaptation. But limiting warming to 2°C will require substantial amounts of mitigation, given that on current trends we are heading for something like 3°C.

If we probe a little deeper, it seems that Lord Lawson's faith in adaptation as a superior strategy is rooted in philosophy rather than in science. In the Adaptation chapter of *An Appeal to Reason*, Lawson quotes a passage from the Nobel Prizewinning economist Friedrich Hayek:[156]

> 'Competition produces an adaptation to countless circumstances which in their totality are not known and cannot be known to any person or authority... We know the general direction of the self-regulating forces of the economy and the general conditions in which these forces will function or not function, but we do now know all the possible circumstances in which they bring about an adaptation. This is impossible because of the general interdependence of the of all parts of the economic process; that is, because, in order to interfere successfully on any point, we would have to know all the details of the whole economy, not only of our own economy but of the world.'

Matt Ridley, too, quotes Hayek approvingly in two of his best-known books, *The Rational Optimist* and

The Evolution of Everything.°

Whatever Hayek's achievements in economics and political philosophy, it is not at all clear how his philosophy is relevant to the real world of science and climate change. To look again at Hayek's paragraph above in the context of climate change: we understand rather well the 'self-regulating forces' of the climate system. But there is abundant evidence that greenhouse gas emissions are already over-riding those forces, to a huge extent. Through our greenhouse gas emissions, we have already 'interfered' with the climate system, and the only choice now is whether to interfere again in an opposite fashion, in order that those self-regulating forces may once again perform their natural function.

Even if humanity does succeed in constraining greenhouse gas emissions significantly, there will need to be a great deal of climate adaptation in the world. Indeed, there already is. In Toronto, health authorities have set up a mechanism to warn carers of the elderly and infirm when dangerously hot days are coming.[157] In West Africa, agricultural scientists have developed new rice varieties resistant to drought.[158] The Netherlands is investigating the idea of covering vast tracts of land with sand as a more natural form of flood defence than seawalls and dykes.[159] There are myriad other examples.

°*The Evolution of Everything* is posited on the notion that developments in society – morality, technology, thought, politics, institutions – are principally adaptive and evolutionary rather than being driven by individual or collective intent

In many cases, especially in the developing world, such developments are positive even in the absence of climate change. The presence of climate change gives them added impetus. But already, it is very clear that adaptation alone cannot deal with all the projected impacts of climate change – and none at all to back the claim that allowing climate change to progress untrammelled and cleaning up the mess afterwards is a superior strategy.

e. <u>*Climate science is bent*</u>

Rhetoric:
'Should Michael Mann be given the electric chair for having concocted arguably the most risibly inept, misleading, cherry-picking, worthless and mendacious graph – the Hockey Stick – in the history of junk science?' – *James Delingpole, Daily Telegraph, April 2013*[160]

Reality:

- Climate change is virtually absent from lists of documented scientific fraud and malpractice
- Mainstream science distilled in the IPCC reports is accepted by all governments, including 'petro-states' that have every economic reason to find fault with them – and by the oil industry
- Independent analyses of the global temperature record have confirmed the existing ones.

All of the arguments advanced thus far fall down if the evidence cannot be trusted. If climate science is bent, then any and all of the preceding four contrarian arguments could be true – perhaps rendering it unnecessary to reduce carbon emissions at all.

The argument that climate science cannot be trusted has cropped up regularly ever since oil company executives first realised its implications for their business models. That statement is not idle rhetoric, but based on one of our young century's most important pieces of journalistic investigation, into the history of Exxon.[161]

But the claim flared up most spectacularly in 2009, as I described in Chapter One, in the episodes that became known as 'ClimateGate' and 'HimalayaGate'.

In the first, the central accusation could hardly have been more fundamental – that leading climate scientists were engaged in a conspiracy to hide reality from the public. The identification of a slowdown in global warming was (at the time) scientifically correct. And the trove of emails hacked from the University of East Anglia (UEA), according to its contrarian distributers, showed that scientists knew the pause was real and were trying to hide it.

Additional claims were that the same set of scientists were manipulating the IPCC by shoe-horning their own scientific papers into its assessment reports; and that they were manipulating the process of peer review, in which science papers are critiqued by other top scientists in the field before publication.

In the UK, three inquiries were set up into the affair. None of them found any evidence of deception.

The Commons Select Committee on Science and Technology concluded that on the accusation that climate scientists were engaged in a deliberate attempt to mislead, there 'was no case to answer'.[162] It did however castigate UEA for a 'culture of non-disclosure' concerning Freedom of Information requests.

The Science Assessment Panel inquiry commissioned by UEA found 'no evidence of any deliberate scientific malpractice,' but recommended that climate science could benefit from a closer working relationship with professional statisticians.[163] Sir Muir Russell's Independent Climate Change Emails Review, the behemoth of the three inquiries at 160 pages, said of the people at the centre of the storm that 'their rigour and honesty as scientists is not in doubt'.[164] It found no evidence of bias in selection of data, no subversion of peer review, and nothing that would undermine the conclusions of the IPCC.

Two inquiries were held into the integrity and practices of the IPCC itself. One, by the Inter-Academy Council, again found no evidence of malpractice but made a number of recommendations aimed at avoiding a repeat of the Himalayan glaciers mistake.[165] The second inquiry was commissioned by the Dutch parliament from the Netherlands Environmental Assessment Agency (PBL) after the IPCC report said that 55 per cent of the Netherlands was vulnerable to flooding. The figure was wrong – but in a somewhat ironic conclusion, PBL found that the error was its own. PBL had included the 55 per cent figure in one of its own reports, which the IPCC then used in its assessment.[166]

Scientists are people. Therefore, they are fallible.

Some may be incompetent. Others may bring instinctive biases to their work. Some may on occasion try to get their own research prioritised in important assessments. So much is human nature. But outright lying and cheating in science is rare – one of the reasons being that unlike in politics (and indeed most areas of journalism), there are formal processes aimed at encouraging evidence-based challenge which act as checks and balances. And there are serious consequences for getting found out.

Peer review is designed to make sure that scientists proffering papers for publication use rational and appropriate methods and reach reasonable conclusions. It does not and cannot verify that the science is correct – but it can and does weed out poor-quality research. At scientific meetings, scientists scrutinise and question each other's research in open session – and it can be ruthless. A scientist who suspects that research done by a peer is faulty can attempt to replicate it – and if they cannot, they can formally publish the criticisms.

The process might not be flawless, but frauds are spotted. In 2004, Korean cloning scientist Hwang Woo-suk claimed in a peer-reviewed paper to have created a line of human embryonic stem cells. Within two months, thanks to scrutiny from his scientific peers and from journalists, it became clear that he had broken ethical guidelines by using cells taken from members of his own team. And within two years, his entire claim was proven fraudulent, leading to dismissal from Seoul National University and eventual imprisonment for embezzlement.[167]

One can look also to Andrew Wakefield, the British gastroenterologist who claimed that the MMR vaccine could cause autism. Later he was found to have had material conflicts of interest, which led to dismissal from London's Royal Free Hospital. Later still, the entire claim was shown to have been false, largely through other researchers repeating his experiments and finding nothing.[168]

In big ticket science, it is vanishingly hard to get away with bogus research.

Literally thousands of scientific papers are published on climate change each year. Occasionally, as in every other branch of science, one is withdrawn, for reasons including misconduct, plagiarism and poor quality. You can see a number listed on the website RetractionWatch – and you will find that they encompass both the mainstream and contrarian schools.[169]

To my knowledge, there has never been a case of malpractice in climate science to rival those of Hwang Woo-suk or Andrew Wakefield. Wikipedia's entry on scientific misconduct includes 58 documented biomedical cases, from Aggarwal to Weiser.[170] They nestle alongside entries for physics, chemistry, plant biology, computer science and the social sciences. For climate change, there is not a single one.

There is also the IPCC, which is undoubtedly the biggest peer review exercise ever undertaken in any branch of research.[171] Government representatives, who technically are the IPCC, meet at the beginning of every six-year Assessment Report cycle and scope out what they want from the next one. They also decide whether they would like to commission special reports, such as the recently-published one on the 1.5°C temperature target. They nominate experts to lead different bits of the various assessments, who assemble further experts nominated by governments into chapter-writing teams with an appropriate balance of country backgrounds and expertise.

Each chapter team collects and collates what it feels are the key relevant pieces of research. They draft the chapters, which then go out for review – not just by other academics, but by people who simply volunteer. Review comments are used to re-draft the report. Eventually a final version is prepared along with a draft Summary for Policymakers (SPM), a document of about 30 pages summarising the main conclusions. The process culminates in a week-long meeting where government representatives go through the SPM line by line together with the lead authors, suggesting (and sometimes demanding) changes, often in talks that run through the night, until, eventually, agreement is reached and the Summary signed off.

This last point is crucial. IPCC reports are not just bunches of material assembled by academics. Governments set the parameters of each assessment, control the budget, collectively commission the academics who will lead it, and approve the conclusions.

When the Fifth Assessment Report was published in 2014, it included a seminally important clause:[172]

> 'Limiting risks across reasons for concern would imply a limit for cumulative emissions of CO_2. Such a limit would require that global net emissions of CO_2 eventually decrease to zero and would constrain annual emissions over the next few decades.'

This statement implies a virtual end to the use of coal, oil and gas (at least, without carbon capture) on a timescale of decades. Its importance lies not in the statement itself, which would be uncontroversial among scientists, but in the fact that it was signed off by every government in the room. This means that oil states such as Saudi Arabia and Iran agreed that the science is basically correct. Tony Abbott's coal-toting government of Australia agreed. So did Russia under sometimes climate sceptic Vladimir Putin, the developing Asian super-states of China and India, and virtually every other country on Earth. And they do not take the sign-off process lightly. The Saudi delegation, for example, is traditionally headed by a senior official from the Ministry of Petroleum.

All of those governments have ample reason to find flaws in the reports, given that coal, oil and gas underpin their economies. And in terms of the details, they do find flaws, which is why the final week's discussions can be so intense. But every time they have gone through the process, they have found no evidence on which to challenge the fundamental point that fossil fuel burning leads to increasing risks of climate change impacts, and that a transition to a low-carbon economy is feasible and desirable.

Let us leave the IPCC for a moment and look at some of the criticisms that are levelled at the broader mass of climate change research.

One is that scientific papers by contrarians are refused for publication in academic journals. This is a claim with great longevity; but it is demonstrably untrue.

In the series of articles on climate scepticism that I

ran on the BBC News website back in 2007, I tried to investigate this by the simple method of openly inviting researchers to send me their stories about 'sceptical' papers that had been rejected, or any other incidents where the institutions of science had been biased against them.[173] I know that my request circulated on contrarian blogs; and as I wrote at the time:

> 'I was expecting a deluge. I anticipated drowning in a torrent of accusations of research grants turned down, membership of the IPCC denied, scientific papers refused by journals, job applications refused, and invitations to speak at conferences drying up.'

The haul was very different. More than 100 people emailed me – but only four had a story to tell, all concerning allegedly rejected papers. Of the four, one sent me a paper that was manifestly incomplete; another was in the process of re-submitting the paper and so declined to send details; and a third was complaining about a journal editor he said was biased in favour of contrarians. Only in one case did the complaint concern an allegedly rejected contrarian paper – but as the scientist had not kept his rejection letters, it was impossible to look into.

And that was it.

Another nail in this coffin of this claim is that papers on climate change angles that depart from the orthodoxy do get published. Henrik Svensmark, the father of the cosmic ray theory of global warming, regularly has papers in reputable journals.[174] Drs John Christy and Roy Spencer between them doubt the cause and likely extent of climate change – in fact, Spencer is an advisor to the Cornwall Alliance, a religious group that holds as an article of faith that: 'There is no convincing scientific evidence that human contribution to greenhouse gases is causing dangerous global warming'.[175,176] But this has not barred them from mainstream science: for decades they have maintained one of the two main satellite records of global temperature at the University of Alabama at Huntsville, and have long lists of publications in scientific journals.[177,178] Both receive US government funding for their work, and Christy has been involved in several IPCC reports.

And the road to formal scientific publication is not blocked to researchers from outside the university system. For example, Nic Lewis, the Bath-based former financier and now independent scientist, has several recent peer-reviewed papers to his name.[179]

By any measure, a properly sceptical look at this favourite contrarian meme shows that it is simply untrue.

Another aspect of the 'you can't trust the scientists' argument is that they form a tiny cabal, peer-reviewing each other's research and helping some 'approved' version of climate science into the IPCC's assessment reports.

In every branch of science and medicine there is a group of academics who sit at the top of their profession – holding the most prestigious university posts, editing journals, advising governments, being called upon by the media. In climate change, the top academics at times exhibit distinctly un-cabal-like behaviour. In the lead-up to this year's IPCC Special Report, for example, a major row blew up over a paper published by a British group of scientists which attempted to calculate the maximum amount of carbon dioxide that can be emitted if governments are to meet their ambition of keeping global warming below 1.5°C.[180]

Their estimate conflicted with others produced by US researchers. Gavin Schmidt, Director of Nasa's Goddard Institute for Space Studies, said the British group's headline claim was 'unsupported' and based on 'globally incomplete estimates [of warming]'.[181] Ben Sanderson of the US National Center for Atmospheric Research said the British team's methodology 'allows for emissions to date to be swept under the carpet.'[182] Both they and the leaders of the UK team, Professors Myles Allen from Oxford University and Michael Grubb from University College London, are absolutely at the top of their profession; but on this point, they definitely did not endorse each other's work uncritically.

Another long-standing row concerns the fate of Arctic sea ice. Most experts in the field believe the Arctic Ocean will start being ice-free in summer around 2040-60. But two – Professors Peter Wadhams of Cambridge University and Wieslaw Maslowski of the Naval Postgraduate School in California – have consistently taken a much more extreme line. Maslowski argued in 2007 that summer sea ice could be gone by 2013, which turned out to be very wide of the mark.[183] Other researchers do not form a 'cabal' around Wadhams and Maslowski – far from it. 'Hasn't Wadhams already predicted four of the last zero ice-free summers?' was one of many sarcastic tweets from other researchers at a recent scientific meeting.[184]

This is exactly how science usually behaves. It shows

researchers being sceptical, in the proper sense of the word.

The scientist who did most to destroy the 'cabal' myth is Professor Richard Muller. A particle physicist who had helped decipher the universe's cosmic microwave background radiation, Muller was expressing concerns about the quality of climate science as long ago as 2004, in the midst of what was then a raging debate about the so-called 'hockey-stick', the graph plotting the Earth's surface temperature with its sharp twentieth century upswing.[185]

After the UEA emails hit the world wide web, Muller decided to go right back to the raw temperature data obtained from weather stations around the world. Using a new methodology, his team would create an entirely fresh temperature record. He assembled a team that included several scientists with no prior experience in the field, such as Nobel prizewinning physicist Saul Perlmutter. If there were problems with the existing records, his Berkeley Earth Project analysis would show them up.

The project met with approval in contrarian circles – perhaps because some of its funding came from the Koch brothers, owners of the US's second biggest privately-held industrial conglomerate and among the biggest funders of paid climate contrarianism.[186]

One who approved enthusiastically was former US weatherman Anthony Watts. At the time, his blog WattsUpWithThat was one of contrarianism's most read and most influential forums. He wrote approvingly of Berkeley Earth's 'superior' methodology, which, he said, 'seems to be a novel approach that handles many of the issues that have been raised.' And, he added: 'I'm prepared to accept whatever result they produce, even if it proves my premise wrong.'[187]

Watts' preparedness to accept the results vanished as soon Muller published them.[188] Far from undermining the existing records, his first Berkeley Earth Surface Temperature (BEST) record confirmed they were right.[189] In Muller's words: 'Our biggest surprise was that the new results agreed so closely with the warming values published previously by other teams in the US and the UK. This confirms that these studies were done carefully and that potential biases identified by climate change sceptics did not seriously affect their conclusions.'

If the scientists who constructed the HadCRUT, NASA and NOAA temperature records had indeed been trying to rig them, they were obviously not very good at it.

Another allegation raised regularly, by *Sunday Telegraph* columnist Christopher Booker among others, is that raw temperature data gathered by weather stations, ships and buoys has routinely been 'fiddled' to make warming appear more than it is. This is, for Booker, 'the biggest science scandal ever.'[190]

Scientists do indeed adjust historical temperature records – with the aim of improving data quality. For example; various methods have been used to take the temperature of seawater from ships. In the early days, people would throw a bucket over the side of a ship, pull it up full of water and stick a thermometer in. Later, thermometers were mounted on the side of the ship or where water comes in to the engine room to cool it. Later still, buoys were deployed; and now, there is the global network of ARGO floats.

When these methods are deployed simultaneously in the same patch of sea, each will give a slightly different raw temperature reading.[191] And as this becomes understood, it is clearly sensible to go back to data recorded in previous decades and correct the raw readings. The same principle applies to temperature data from weather stations on land, where (for example) the time of day when measurements are recorded may have changed, or where electronic instruments have replaced old mercury thermometers.[192]

Booker is right that in some cases, this leads to the rate of global warming at a given location being adjusted upwards. But by no means in all. The adjustment that has the biggest effect is that for sea surface temperatures. And here, the effect of corrections has been to make global warming seem *slower* than it was when the raw data was used. Which would be very strange behaviour for a group of scientists intending to make climate change seem more scary. As Berkeley Earth's Zeke Hausfather has shown, the net effect of all the adjustments taken together is virtually zero after 1950, and decreases the amount of long-term warming in the record prior to that. [193]

Booker also sometimes dips into the argument most consistently espoused by Anthony Watts – that the raw temperature data is inherently unreliable because weather stations are sometimes located in areas that have become progressively more urbanised. Urban environments are inherently warmer than rural ones, because tarmac and concrete absorb and store more heat than rural land. So, Watts argues, when thermometers register a rising temperature, the real driver is increasing urbanisation rather than global warming.

This 'urban heat island' effect is well-known, and the link that Watts proposes has been well-studied. And disproven, in study after study after study. In 2005, David Parker of the UK Met Office found that the rise in night-time temperatures was identical during windy and calm conditions.[194] Were the temperature rise down to urbanisation you would expect calm nights to show a greater rise, because wind disperses the heat.

In 2008, researchers showed that urbanisation had contributed about 0.1°C to temperature increases registered by Chinese weather stations; global warming had contributed at least eight times as much.[195] In 2009, US researchers compared the warming records from 'well-situated' and 'poorly-situated' weather stations – and found that both showed the same record of warming, with the well-situated ones in fact registering slightly more than the others.[196] Another study in the US found that urban stations were warming a bit faster than rural stations in the raw data, but this had already been effectively detected and corrected by researchers.[197] Finally, in 2013 the BEST team divided records from nearly 37,000 weather stations across the world into those located near urban areas and those not. The rates of warming were identical between the two sets. [198]

Alleged problems with data from thermometers have led contrarians to claim that the temperature record derived from satellite readings is somehow inherently superior. It has been convenient, because at times satellite records have indicated that the world is warming more slowly than those from weather stations.

There are two satellite records in common use – the RSS record from Remote Sensing Systems in California, and the UAH record from the University of Alabama at Huntsville kept by Roy Spencer and John Christy.[199,200]

Satellites do not measure temperature directly. Instead they measure microwave radiation coming upwards from oxygen molecules at different levels in the atmosphere. From these readings, scientists must reconstruct the temperature. The advantage satellites offer is that depending on their orbit, they can monitor the entire world, without the data 'holes' associated with the lack of weather stations in Polar regions, Africa and the ocean. Disadvantages are:

- The record goes back only to 1979
- The instruments cannot produce a true surface temperature record but instead are deducing the average temperature over a 'smeared' column of atmosphere from the surface up to 7km[201]
- The instruments can 'drift' over time, losing their initial calibration, making their readings increasingly unreliable.

This last point in particular has led to much greater corrections being applied to satellite records than to those from weather stations. One adjustment resulted in the rate of warming increasing by 2.4 times.[202] If adjustments to surface temperature records are 'the biggest scientific scandal ever', in Booker's phrase, what then should be contrarians' reaction to those made to satellite readings? Certainly not, logically speaking, to claim they are inherently superior to surface-based records.

The final body blow to the notion that climate science is crooked comes from the natural world.

Let us for a moment accept the most extreme version of the contrarian argument. Let us assume that most climate scientists are either incompetent or bent, or both. (That is already tens of thousands of people across the world, most of them quite clever and independent-minded – but still – bear with me.)

We then need to assume that all the arguments between climate scientists are irrelevant, or just for show.

If we want, we can add in the claim that the entire 'scare story' is funded by 'shadowy' green billionaires in thrall to Al Gore. (We need to ignore the evidence of the kinds of houses that scientists live in and what cars they drive – but bear with me still.)

We need to believe that the government delegates who commission, scrutinise and eventually endorse the IPCC reports are all either stupid or in on the green conspiracy, including those from the Saudi Ministry of Petroleum. And that the bosses of all the businesses from Walmart to Statoil who accept the scientific evidence on climate change are also stupid or are doing it to look good.

One question still remains: what about the plants and animals? Who brought them into the conspiracy, and how?

There are literally thousands of pieces of evidence that fish, frogs, plankton, butterflies, birds and other creatures are shifting their range, either Polewards or upwards. Spring is coming earlier and autumn leaving later, with plants blooming accordingly and growing seasons lengthening. The pattern is utterly consistent with a warming world.

Contrarians sometimes allege that climate change is 'the biggest conspiracy in history'. If someone has found a way of involving the plant and animal kingdoms in the conspiracy, they are surely right.

f. *We can't afford it*

Rhetoric:

'Unless those who rule us come down out of cloud cuckoo land very fast (abandon the Climate Change Act), our lights will go out, our computers will shut down, our economy will judder to a halt and we shall face a national catastrophe.' – *Christopher Booker, Sunday Telegraph, July 2008*[203]

Reality:

- Renewables are now the cheapest source of electricity generation to build in at least 60 nations
- There is no evidence that climate change and energy policies are driving industry away from the UK or Europe
- Since 1992, the UK leads the G7 in both per-capita emissions reductions and per-capita economic growth.

A central plank of the contrarian worldview is that tackling climate change is fundamentally unaffordable. It holds that renewable energy, for example, is always going to be more expensive than fossil fuelled generation, and that British industry will basically shut down as high prices force companies abroad. Lord Lawson has gone so far as to claim that a clean energy transition will return us to 'pre-industrial standards of living'. And as it is so expensive, the argument goes, Britain is wrong to be trying it, and developing countries will never do so.

Forecasting the costs of a transition to clean energy has proven not to be easy. Much forecasting comes from computer models of the economy that are, for example, unable to capture the kind of 'disruption' being produced right now by the unforeseen dive in renewable energy costs.

The plummeting price of solar – a fall of about 70 per cent in five years – was not predicted even by long-time advocates such as Greenpeace.[204] And what you cannot foresee, you cannot put into an economic model. Not foreseeing price reductions means over-estimating the cost of switching to clean energy compared with sticking with fossil fuels. As an aside, the models are also poor at capturing side-benefits of reducing emissions, for example by decreasing the health costs of air pollution.

In 2008, there was already some evidence that cutting emissions need not harm the economy. The UN climate convention was by then 16 years old; in that period Britain had cut its carbon emissions by 18 per cent while posting economic growth of 56 per cent.[205,206] The same pattern of a growing economy and shrinking emissions held true for Germany, Denmark, Sweden and a number of other European countries.[p]

A principal driver of UK emission cuts in that period was the 'dash for gas', in which electricity generation switched from coal-fired power stations (historically, as with coal mines, state-owned) to more flexible (and privately-owned) gas generation. It is somewhat ironic that Nigel Lawson, as an architect of the dash for gas, contributed so significantly to reducing UK carbon emissions; but there it is. But the biggest transformation in any sector was a virtual halving of methane emissions from waste in landfill sites[207] – showing the impact that targeted policies can have.

However, in 2008, there were legitimate reasons to query the costs of decarbonisation. A coal-to-gas transition might reduce carbon dioxide emissions somewhat, but could not be a long-term player in achieving the at-least-80 per cent emissions cut by 2050 enshrined in the Climate Change Act. Renewable energy was expensive in 2008 – studies came to various conclusions, but it would not have been unreasonable to argue that electricity from a new onshore wind farm would cost half as much again as from a new gas-fired power station.[208] Building new nuclear power stations seemed fraught with political and economic uncertainties; there were concerns about biofuels' impact on nature and food security, and electric

---

[p] The most spectacular rates of decarbonisation were seen in former Soviet bloc countries after 1991 – but these were caused by economic collapse, rather than running alongside economic growth as in Western Europe

vehicles belonged in either dairies or science-fiction movies.

In sectors such as iron and steel, European companies were being out-competed on cost by firms in Asia, and there were fears that this would increase if decarbonisation drove up energy prices. The point was made that this would also have a perverse impact on global carbon emissions, by transferring production in reasonably regulated western factories to counterparts in the developing world that would probably be much less efficient.

The British government produced an Impact Assessment for the Climate Change Act.[209] The cost of meeting the headline cut of at least 80 per cent it estimated at £324-404bn over the 43 years to 2050.

It is a big number. But over 43 years, it comes in at less than £10bn per year. In 2017, for comparison, Britain spent £102bn on education, £155bn on health and £252bn on social protection; those figures are just for public expenditure, so are underestimates.[210] With UK GDP a little under £2 trillion per year,[211] funding the clean energy transition amounts to less than one per cent of national income – pretty much what the Stern Review forecast. And of course this is not wasted money – it goes into sustaining companies and employing workers, so re-entering the economy.

If you choose not to accept the scientific evidence on climate change or take a Panglossian lens to its likely impacts, this will probably seem like a foolish use of money. If you accept the evidence, it may seem rather modest. These are value judgements, after all.

The costs of clean energy can seem much higher than they are because of serial misuse of a single word

– 'subsidy'. The main method for funding the zero-carbon energy rollout in the UK is now a mechanism called Contracts for Difference (CfDs). These contracts guarantee a fixed price for electricity from wind farms or nuclear reactors. When the market price for electricity is lower than this fixed price, the generator receives the difference between the two from the Low-Carbon Contracts Company, the agency that administers CfDs for the government. If the market price is higher, the generator pays the difference back.

CfDs are often mis-labelled as 'subsidies'; you may read, for example, that the new nuclear power station at Hinckley point will receive a 'subsidy' of £92.50/MWh. This is plain wrong. The real subsidy is the difference, averaged over time, between the guaranteed price and the market price.

As the price of wind and solar power come down, the subsidies are shrinking rapidly. In the last CfD round for offshore wind farms, two projects were awarded contracts at £57.50/MWh. As my ECIU colleague Dr Jonathan Marshall and I showed, the subsidy involved in this contract is a mere £4/MWh.[212] If the wholesale price of gas continues to rise and pushes up the wholesale price of electricity, these wind farms will end up receiving a 'negative subsidy'; were new onshore wind farms to be awarded CfDs, this would already be the case.[213]

The *Financial Times* recently agreed that labelling the entire CfD amount a 'subsidy' was misleading and pledged not to do it any more.[214] Not everyone has caught up.

One number entrenched in contrarian circles is that the Climate Change Act will cost the UK more than

£300bn by 2030 (not by 2050 as the government forecast). It comes from a report written for GWPF by Peter Lilley, the former Secretary of State for Trade and Industry and former deputy leader of the Conservative Party.[215] So appealing was it to Conservative politicians that it ended up in the manifesto for the 2017 General Election – the UKIP manifesto, that is.[216]

Lilley arrives at his figure through a number of assumptions that are hard or impossible to justify. The *CarbonBrief* website has published a full analysis, and I will not repeat the exercise here.[217] Three examples will serve to show that the figure has no basis in fact:

- Lilley puts 'the impact of the carbon dioxide emissions tax on electricity prices alone' in 2050 at £1,390 per household.[q] But in 2050, if the UK meets its 2050 climate change target, electricity generation will be almost entirely zero-carbon – hence it will incur virtually no carbon tax at all
- He entirely ignores economic benefits of decarbonisation in areas such as improved health and reduced traffic congestion, and in building forward-looking British companies which can export low-carbon goods and services
- He says 'there is no guarantee' that 'deployment of low-carbon technologies will lead to a fall in their costs as they mature.' Even at the time of writing (2016) this was clearly wrong, as costs of solar and

---

[q] Government projections usually include a steadily rising carbon tax, although it is by no means certain that successive governments will make this happen

wind power had consistently fallen; it is even more glaringly wrong now given the halving of prices for new offshore wind contracts in just two years.[218]

Two other claims crop up in Lilley's report and elsewhere that need a comment. One is that adding wind and solar power to the grid entails vast 'hidden costs' in the form of reserve generation needed when wind and solar output is low. Lilley argues that this will effectively add 30-50 per cent to the price of renewable energy.

This is not backed up by the conclusions of academic studies. The UK Energy Research Centre (UKERC) recently published a review of evidence from the past decade, finding that: '...the additional cost of these reserves remains relatively modest, at least up to a 30 per cent variable renewable penetration level, with the majority of results being £5/MWh or less.'[219] Taken as a proportion of the latest price in offshore wind contracts – £57.50/MWh – this is 10 per cent, not the 30-50 per cent that Lilley claims. UKERC points out that 'conventional' generation also incurs 'hidden costs' – for example, power stations that have to be kept spinning but not feeding power to the grid in case another power station unexpectedly fails.

Other recent analyses have further holed the claim that renewable energy carries 'vast hidden costs'. The consultancy Aurora Energy Research found that adding more solar power to the system would, on its own, increase costs.[220] But adding solar plus battery storage would bring the overall cost *down* – if you like, a 'hidden benefit'. And the National Infrastructure Commission found that adding flexibility (such as storage) to a renewables-based electricity system would reduce the national electricity bill by up to £8bn a year by 2030.[221]

The other most obviously unsupportable claim that Lilley highlights is that manufacturing industries are fleeing the country because of 'cripplingly' high energy prices. (Use of the word 'cripplingly' appears mandatory in contrarian circles when fulminating about high energy costs, just as the word 'shadowy' is regularly deployed for any organisation campaigning for emission cuts.)

Electricity bills for the highest-consuming UK businesses have been among the largest in Europe (though gas bills have not). This is not, however, entirely down to the costs of the clean energy transition. Wholesale energy prices and network costs have also been cited as causes.[222] And recent policy changes have given intensive energy users almost total exemption from energy policy levies on bills.

Most importantly, there is no evidence that energy prices have driven industry from the UK's shores. The highest profile example in recent years has been Tata Steel, whose UK operations came close to collapse in 2015. After exemptions, energy policy levies accounted for less than one per cent of Tata's steelmaking costs. Other factors acknowledged by Tata to be far more important include labour costs 20 times higher than those in China, pension liabilities higher than it had realised when buying the operation a decade earlier, the strong pound, and weak domestic demand.[223,224] The biggest factor of all was a halving of the European steel price over just four years, as struggling Chinese producers flooded the global market with cheap steel.[225]

Certain types of business do relocate from the developed world to the developing. But energy costs are not the cause. Energy bills were not a factor in the relocation of call-centres from Europe to India and Rwanda; neither does Apple buy computer chips from Chinese factories rather than British ones because energy is cheaper in China. Study after study has failed to find any evidence that companies are moving abroad due to the costs of a clean energy transition. Even the House of Lords Economic Affairs Committee, on which GWPF Trustee Lord (Andrew) Turnbull sits, was forced to conclude in its 2017 inquiry into UK energy policy:

> 'There is currently no robust and reliable data on whether measures to reduce the UK's carbon emissions have in fact resulted in the same emissions being exported to other countries due to the closure or relocation of energy intensive industries.'[226]

As far as I aware, Turnbull has not yet, in the light of this conclusion, gone back to the foreword he wrote for Peter Lilley's GWPF report and corrected his erroneous assertion that the Climate Change Act means that energy-intensive industries are 'progressively being relocated abroad'.[227]

Ten years ago, we had to rely on forecasts of what a low-carbon transition might cost. Now, we can look back at a decade of real-world data.

From 2008 to 2017 – the decade of the Climate Change Act – the British economy grew by 12 per cent.[228] In the same period, its greenhouse gas emissions fell by 30 per cent.[229] The 2008 financial crash triggered by the collapse of Northern Rock has probably made the growth number less striking than it would otherwise have been and the emission reduction number more striking. Either way, it is a remarkable finding, and one than proves beyond any reasonable doubt that, thus far, cutting greenhouse gas emissions has not proven ruinous for the UK economy.

Perhaps the most remarkable statistic is that over the 10 years since Britain introduced the Climate Change Act and Nigel Lawson published *An Appeal to Reason*, the average Briton's energy bill has fallen. Even as levies on bills funded construction of 9,000-odd wind turbines, put more than a million subsidised solar panels on homes and upgraded the pipes and cables that supply homes and businesses, the average household energy bill fell by about 10 per cent.[230] During that time, not only did coal's share of the generation mix plummet to just 7 per cent, the amount of electricity that we obtained from gas-fired generation fell by a quarter.[231]

One factor that contrarians traditionally miss, ignore or dispute is that emissions have come down because we use energy less wastefully.[r] Boilers, cookers and other appliances have all become more efficient – partly through competition between suppliers, partly through innovation, and partly through rules and regulations.

---

[r] Lilley goes so far as to contend that 'the aim of climate policy is to reduce carbon dioxide emissions, not to reduce energy consumption' – a claim utterly at odds with the reality in many countries which seek energy efficiency improvements as the first element of climate policy

Energy companies have been obliged to help the poorest households waste less energy, for example through installing insulation. Banning incandescent lightbulbs forced the industry that once invented planned obsolescence to innovate and create equally usable but far more efficient alternatives.[232] Bulbs that will last a human lifespan are not too far off.[233]

Lilley claims that all of this would have happened by itself without funded interventions. While some of it probably would have, the importance of policy can be seen in the fact that a recent regressive change has slashed the current rate of UK home insulation by 95 per cent.[234]

In reality, we can never know whether in the absence of climate legislation the UK economy would have grown by marginally more or less. Nevertheless, cutting emissions has emphatically not brought economic hardship. In per-capita terms, Britain leads the G7 bloc of nations on both economic growth and emission cuts since the UN climate convention came into being in 1992.[235]

Myriad factors are responsible, many of which lie outside the arena of climate change and energy policy. Nevertheless, the argument that the Climate Change Act facilitates economically rational policymaking does have logical force; and it could be that Britain's planning of emission cutting measures, more systematic than most, has helped maintain economic progress compared against other nations' more piecemeal approaches. In terms of both growing the economy and cutting greenhouse gas emissions, neither Germany nor the US – neither of which has a Climate Change Act – can boast progress anything like as good since 2008.[236]

The contrast with Germany illustrates the point. Germany's long-term target is to cut emissions by 95 per cent by 2050. But it has nothing like the Climate Change Act that sets interim targets to drive policymaking, and no independent scrutineer to hold government to account. Coal and car companies and their trade unions have lobbied successfully to keep existing business models going as long as possible. Without an effective tool to force progress in these two crucial sectors, Germany's carbon emissions are currently flat-lining.[237]

The future is not the past. Some areas of the economy are easier to decarbonise than others, with agriculture, aviation and some industries among the most difficult. Phasing out coal has delivered an estimated 80 per cent of Britain's carbon emission reductions in the last five years. Once it is complete, ministers will need to get serious about higher-hanging fruit.

Even so, looking into the real world, it is irrefutable that the contrarians' prophecy that the Climate Change Act would be 'a monstrous act of self-harm' have so far been conclusively disproven.

g. The lights will go out

Rhetoric:

'In August 1914, Sir Edward Grey famously said, "The lamps are going out all over Europe". He was speaking of the war we had inflicted on ourselves. A century later, we are threatening

to put them out again, with different motives, but equal folly.' – *Charles Moore, Daily Telegraph, October 2014*[238]

Reality:

- Britain sources more than half of its electricity from low-carbon generation – almost 20 per cent from variably-generating wind and solar. The lights have stayed on
- The incidence of power cuts is declining even as more renewables are added to the system
- Several countries obtain even more of their electricity (above 40%) from wind and solar than the UK, with no reliability issues.

I must declare a bit of *mea culpa* here: I helped start this one. In 2005, as a relative newcomer to BBC national broadcasting after many years at World Service, I covered a seminar organised by Professor John Loughhead, then head of the UK Energy Research Council.[239] The UK was facing an electricity supply crisis, experts said (and I reported).[240] Nuclear and coal-fired power stations would be closing over the next decade, and Britain had no plan to build new ones; without such a plan, the lights would, at some point, go out.

If this claim seems familiar – well, it should. A decade after I penned my small chapter in the 'Blackout Britain' narrative, the first report from the organisation that I now run, the Energy and Climate Intelligence Unit (ECIU), looked back at such claims in the UK press and at their relationship with reality.[241] We found that newspapers had published more than 500 articles in that decade claiming that Britain was at risk of blackouts.[s]

Sometimes we were warned that the lights would go out in the coming winter; sometimes D for Darkness Day lay a few years hence. In many cases, the articles claimed that the lights would go out unless we invested in a particular technology – and thus it is reasonably easy to guess where the story originated. Shale gas and nuclear power were the two most visible such lobbies – although British Gas chief Sam Laidlaw comfortably won the 'brass neck' award by warning in 2014 that the lights might go out if regulator Ofgem proceeded with an inquiry into whether the 'Big Six' energy utilities were colluding to keep energy bills high.[242] The biggest of the six is, of course, British Gas.

Many of the articles attributed the blackout risk to the switch from dispatchable power stations running on coal, gas and nuclear fission to variably-generating wind farms and solar panels.[t] Others fulminated about energy policy in general. Towards the end of the decade, an emergent feature of coverage was the clusters of 'Blackout Britain' stories seen twice each year, in July and October, when National Grid releases its forecasts of how generation will stack up against demand for the coming winter.

---

[s] I am sure that broadcasters made such claims over the same period at a similar rate, but the contents of past radio and TV programmes is far harder to access and analyse

[t] 'Dispatchable' power stations are those that can be turned on and off at will

Compared with this tide of rhetoric, the reality was startling different. During that decade – in fact, as far back as we could trace – Britain did not have a single power cut attributable to a lack of generation capacity. Only one single outage was in any way attributable to a generation issue – in May 2008, when two big power stations, Longannet and Sizewell B, tripped out within five minutes of each other, for unrelated reasons.

Even then, back-up mechanisms should have been able to cope; but incorrectly set sensors then caused reserve generators to trip out. As a protective measure, distribution network operators (DNOs) shut down power to 580,000 homes for an average duration of 20 minutes.[u]

And that was it. Despite the 500+ doom-mongering headlines, the lights had not actually gone out once as a consequence of a shortage of generation.

Britain does have power cuts – in the order of a quarter of a million per year. But they are not caused by an absence of shale gas wells or new nuclear power stations, by the advent of renewable energy or interventions in the market. In 2013/14, National Grid reported 44 outages due to faults on its high-voltage national network, about half caused by weather conditions such as lightning or high winds. The remaining power cuts all stemmed from faults in the DNOs' regional cable networks that carry power to

---

[u] The companies that operate regional low-voltage networks, carrying power from National Grid's high-voltage nationwide system to homes and businesses

homes and businesses.[v] Typical causes include contractors putting shovels through cables, wind bringing down power lines or sub-station relays being tripped by flooding. Many of these interruptions last longer than the 20 minutes experienced during the freak Longannet-Sizewell outage. But for whatever reasons you choose to conjure up, these quarter of a million real annual power cuts receive vanishingly little media attention, in marked contrast to those that do not exist.

Not only have there been no power cuts from lack of generation, the number of close calls is also declining. If National Grid foresees a period coming when the cushion between available generation and demand might not be comfortable, it can circulate an Electricity Margin Notice.[w] In the years leading up to 2015, while coal-fired and nuclear power stations were closing down, wind farms springing up across the nation and contrarian commentators warning of blackout doom, National Grid issued fewer and fewer such warnings – an average of nine per year 2005-2008, fewer than one per year 2013-2016.[243]

The 2016-17 winter ought logically to have been stressful. Three of Britain's big coal-fired stations had just closed, the interconnecting cable able to import electricity from France was out of action, and a large

---

[v] These, too, are becoming even more reliable, with several DNOs reporting year-on-year falls in the incidence and duration of outages

[w] Before 2016, called a Notice of Insufficient System Margin or NISM

chunk of the French nuclear fleet was in any case closed due to reactor safety concerns. Yet National Grid issued not a single tight margin warning; neither has it done since.

Looking across the entire media piece – from home affairs to business, from education to the arts, from health to sport, from foreign affairs to Westminster politics – I cannot think of any other issue where the dominant UK media narrative has been so diametrically opposed to reality.

If you are wondering how this relates to climate change, the point is that for politicians, worries about the lights going out in the next year or two will always trump longer-term concerns about climate change. And if a government scales back support for decarbonisation – if a nation invests less in energy efficiency, renewables, nuclear power and flexibility – the result will be that we burn more gas. So, successful scare-mongering about 'blackouts' can achieve the same objective as undermining climate science.

Now, the UK has the Capacity Market – set up precisely to make sure that there is enough dispatchable generation to meet peak demand, through auctions that pay for it to be available through the winter.[244] The auctions run four years ahead of delivery. That is ample time in which the market could fund a new gas-fired power station, say, if any were needed. Yet, in four years of auctions, they have not been needed.

Eggborough coal-fired power station in Nottinghamshire announced its closure in February this year after it repeatedly failed to win Capacity Market contracts.[245] Simply, Eggborough is surplus to requirements – Britain has enough non-renewable generating capacity without it. And the government can continue using the Capacity Market for as long as it chooses. As Steve Holliday, formerly CEO of National Grid for 12 years, told the BBC Today Programme during the 2017 Capacity Market auction: 'It's time for the headline of "Blackout Britain" to end – it's simply wrong. We've been talking about blackouts for 15 years every time it gets cold, but it's a scare story. The lights haven't gone out yet and thanks to the measures the government is putting in place this week they definitely won't go out in future.'[246]

In the long run, if Britain (or any other country) simply replaced dispatchable power stations with wind farms and solar panels that do not generate on demand, then at some point the lights really would go out. But this is not the reality.

For a number of reasons, including cost and climate change, most countries are now heading inexorably towards an electricity system where the bulk of generation comes from renewables. In Britain, wind will dominate; globally, solar is set to become the single biggest technology. But there is no technical reason why a renewables-heavy generation mix will lead to shortages. The key is to also invest in the four so-called 'flexibility mechanisms':

- Demand-shifting, also known as demand-side response, in which real-time price information incentivises consumers to switch non-time-critical usage away from periods when demand and hence prices are high
- Storage, in batteries, pumped hydro or other

technologies

- International trading (in the case of island Britain, via undersea cables)
- Peaking generation – (usually) gas-fired power stations designed to turn on and off quickly, to be used rarely and for short periods.

Britain uses all four of these mechanisms already, and there is much more to come. Four interconnecting cables currently link the UK grid to other European countries. A further seven are due to be operating by 2022, with yet more on the drawing board if there is a market for them.[247] The country possesses 2.8 GW of pumped hydro storage stations, and businesses are planning more as the grid becomes more flexible.[248,249] If the market allows, the two technologies could in principle work together – for example, Scandinavian countries, with their sparse populations and huge resources, might invest in more pumped hydro to provide flexibility for the UK and other European nations.

Battery storage is being built at different scales – in homes, in businesses, by DNOs and by National Grid. If government gets the 'smart' charging infrastructure for electric vehicles right so that car-owners can trade energy with the grid when their vehicles are plugged in, that would create a nationwide 'distributed battery'. The size of this battery will depend on how technology and markets evolve. But by one estimate, if all Britain's cars were electric – which is likely by 2050 – having a mere one per cent of the fleet plugged in smartly would provide enough capacity to meet about one-fifth of today's peak electricity demand.[250]

As far as I am aware, the first warning that a transition to renewables would risk the lights going out was sounded by the chairman of ELTRA, which then ran the electricity network in western Denmark. In 2003 he said: 'We said that the electricity system could not function if wind power increased above 500 MW. Now we are handling almost five times as much. And... we are ready to handle even more, but it requires that we are allowed to use the right tools to manage the system.'[251]

Since then, Denmark's wind power capacity has virtually doubled again. And its energy security is ranked fifth in the world.[252]

Denmark sources more of its power from variable renewables than any other EU nation, at 43 per cent.[253] Germany, Ireland, Portugal and Spain are all above the 20 per cent mark, with the UK fast catching up at 18 per cent. In all of them, the lights are staying on.

In the last couple of years, the 'lights are going out' narrative has become much more muted. As with denial of climate change, it is simply not feasible for even the most one-eyed backbench MP or media commentator to promote a line that is so obviously not true. Winters come, winters go, and the lights stay on. People notice this kind of thing.

h. Britain is going it alone – no-one else will follow us

Rhetoric:

'The United Kingdom is completely isolated in this.' – *Nigel Lawson, House of Lords, Nov 2008*[254]

Reality:

- In 2015, 195 nations concluded the Paris Agreement, under which virtually every one pledged to constrain its greenhouse gas emissions
- Several countries have introduced climate change legislation reflecting the UK Act
- Some are going further, pledging to reach 'net zero' emissions by mid-century.

The argument that Britain was 'going it alone' in tackling climate change was more than a little spurious even in 2008, because Britain never had been 'going it alone'. By the time that *An Appeal to Reason* reached the bookshelves, the United Nations climate convention had been in existence for 15 years and the Kyoto Protocol for more than a decade.[x] Under the Protocol, all developed nations and 'economies in transition' pledged to cut or at least limit emissions.[255,256] The European Union agreed to cut emissions by 8 per cent by the period 2008-12, the US and Canada by 7 per cent, and Japan to 6 per cent.

Nevertheless, there was a degree of legitimacy in the argument in that Britain was preparing to be the first nation to set a decarbonisation target in law. If you are the first to do something, of course no-one else may follow.

To a certain extent, the debacle at the Copenhagen summit a year later seemed to back Lawson's contention. Certainly it confirmed that most nations

---

[x] Although it did not come into force until 2005

were not ready for a binding international agreement. Even so, many developing nations that had not previously pledged to constrain their emissions set targets under the Copenhagen Accord. No country weakened its existing ambitions.

As a bloc, the EU has continued to meet all of its targets, despite the failures of several individual member states. The US and China are also on track to meet their Copenhagen pledges.

The argument that 'no-one else will follow' falls down even more clearly when measured against the huge diplomatic triumph that is the Paris Agreement. Secured in December 2015, this marked the first time that virtually all governments pledged to constrain their greenhouse gas emissions. Countries made different types of commitment depending on their level of prosperity: rich ones set reduction targets, those less prosperous typically pledged to reduce their rate of emissions growth prior to making cuts later.

The form of China's pledge is typical of fast-developing nations in that it commits to reduce carbon intensity – the emissions associated with each unit of GDP – by 60-65 per cent by 2030.[257] China went further than many by also pledging to peak its emissions around 2030 at the latest.

If you see climate change as an existential issue, the Paris Agreement is far from perfect. Although governments committed to hold global warming 'well below 2°C' and to 'pursue efforts' to keep it under 1.5°C, they did not pledge emission cuts that can deliver on that commitment.

There are numerous other holes as well. In some people's eyes, the absence of any mechanism that can force governments to meet their pledges is a gaping void. But certainly the contrarian claim that the Agreement is useless because it does not 'force' developing nations to reduce their emissions does not hold water. You can imagine also the reaction of UK contrarians had UK ministers signed an international agreement that allowed China and India to 'force' Britain to reduce its emissions.

For anyone who does not follow the international negotiations on climate change in detail, it is easy to miss just how significant the Paris Summit was. Six years beforehand, governments had signally failed to conclude a global agreement in desolate Copenhagen; in the bloody aftermath, it was entirely possible to see the UN climate process falling apart completely. Yet just two years later, at the Durban summit in 2011, governments agreed to try again; and four years later they delivered. The detailed reasons for the turnaround would fill up another book entirely, but they can perhaps be summed up in three points:

- Real world evidence of the risks of climate change was stronger than ever, rooted in vindication of mainstream science after the UEA email hack, a strong showing by the IPCC's Fifth Assessment Report in 2013-14, and the record-breaking temperatures of 2014 and 2015
- Real world evidence that clean energy costs were plummeting was coming thick and fast, topped by the 70 per cent fall in the cost of solar power over five years
- Serious, mature and consistent diplomatic activity led by the US and France, with China as a willing

partner, persuaded doubtful governments that here was a genuinely global effort worth joining.

The majority of contrarian campaigners and commentators do not follow the UN process in any detail at all – which is probably why they missed the significance.

Another fact usually missed by contrarians is that countries do not sign up to such agreements because they are forced to – they do so because they want to. To a large extent, the Paris Agreement exists because it aligns with the national development priorities of most nations – certainly of big ones such as China and India.

These two Asian behemoths are embarking on a vast clean energy transition (more on this in the final chapter). This is not only prompted by climate change. Other factors include:

- The swiftly falling price of renewable energy
- The social and economic imperative for clean air
- The desire to build the industries that will dominate the twenty-first century, such as electric cars and solar panels, rather than those that led in the twentieth
- Energy independence (whatever Vladimir Putin may do, he will never control the sun and the wind).

To say that China and India are taking these steps because they are following Britain's lead would be a huge exaggeration. But there is no doubt that Britain's early adoption of a legally-binding emissions target was a case of leading by example. British diplomacy and expertise have been factors in persuading and assisting other countries down a clean growth pathway. Mexican politicians have come to London to find out how the Climate Change Act works. British civil servants have gone to China to explain how the Committee on Climate Change, the world's first independent statutory climate change watchdog, works. British technocrats and academics have played a very significant role in what you might call 'technical diplomacy' for over a decade, almost always without fanfare, and in doing so have helped many developing nations draw up their own plans for a clean energy transition.

Within the European Union, a somewhat different story has emerged. The bloc's central ambition is to cut emissions by 80-95 per cent by 2050 – almost identical to the UK's national commitment, set at almost the same point in time. So, to follow for a moment longer the thread of Lord Lawson's argument, we need to ask whether Britain, with its Climate Change Act, has fared worse than the EU over the last decade:

- European Union: 7% GDP growth, 17% fall in greenhouse gas emissions[258]
- United Kingdom: 12% GDP growth, 30% fall in greenhouse gas emissions.

If indeed no other nation has followed the UK in implementing a Climate Change Act, that would appear to be their loss.

Because the British approach is logical, systematic and cost-effective, other countries are now drawing from it. Within the last three years, Finland and Sweden have introduced climate change laws largely modelled on the UK Act.[259,260] Further afield, New

Zealand is even now doing the same thing.[261]

Sweden has gone further than the UK. Its Climate Change Act mandates annual carbon budgets rather than five-yearly ones. And the goal is not merely to cut greenhouse gas emissions, but to end them: a 'net zero' target under which Sweden's net contribution to climate change finishes by 2045. New Zealand is also likely to set a net zero emissions goal in law, probably by 2050. France, Iceland, Norway and Costa Rica are among the other nations that have made a political commitment to a net zero economy by 2050 at the latest, without yet indicating whether they will set the target in law.

So not only has Lawson's contention turned out to be wrong – Britain has not been going it alone – it was also asking the wrong question. Rather than harming the economy, the UK's Climate Change Act has, if anything benefited it; so much so that other countries are following the model, and in some cases going beyond it.

It is of course far from certain that governments will take all of the action they have pledged. And to meet the goals of the Paris Agreement, they will have to do that and a lot more.

But it is equally clear that the vast majority are concerned about climate change and have plans to curb carbon emissions; equally clear too that clean technologies are advancing at a rate unsuspected just a few years back, which may enable a quicker low-carbon transition than governments currently feel is possible. But as things stand, predictions that no other countries would curb their greenhouse gas emissions and enact a clean energy transition have already proved demonstrably wrong, given that this is exactly what they are doing.

3
Journalism eats itself

In 2017, the distinguished political commentator Peter Oborne gave an interview to Greenpeace's investigative spin-off *Unearthed* in which he laid a serious charge against the UK's right-leaning newspapers.[262] The press, he said, had 'failed' on climate change: 'The right has been culpable for not treating this as a serious matter.' He continued:

> 'I think I was rather too impressed by climate sceptics to begin with. I'm in favour of scepticism, you see. But the evidence now is overwhelming. We have galloping climate change.'

It is easy to see why people would be impressed by the UK's leading climate contrarians, for they are impressive people. Nigel Lawson and Peter Lilley have held high-ranking cabinet posts. Lawson and Matt Ridley are members of the House of Lords; both write with enviable ease and grace. All can command a room.

But that does not make them right.

Peter Oborne's critique is especially telling because his career lies at the heart of the right-leaning press – as political editor of *The Spectator*, chief political commentator for the *Daily Telegraph*, and now a political commentator with the *Daily Mail*.

But he is not alone in his charge. The House of Commons Science and Technology Select Committee came to a similar conclusion four years ago, in a report that included the damning statement: '...opinion pieces about climate science in these publications are frequently based on factual inaccuracies which go unchallenged.'[263] On the website Climate Feedback, scientists regularly fact-check articles in British mainstream titles and find them wanting.[264] Newspapers and the BBC have been obliged by their own complaints processes and by regulators to correct misleading coverage, which in many cases could have been avoided by simple fact-checking in advance of publication.

If we adopt Oborne's premise, then the question is – why?

I think that the roots lie in the years at the end of the 2000s. Then, at 'official' level, climate change seemed like a 'done deal'. The broad outline of the science seemed settled. The Stern Review had painted a picture in which it was economically rational to curb greenhouse gas emissions as quickly as possible, the Climate Change Act had passed with astonishing consensus, and the international community was apparently committed to forging a new global political agreement at the Copenhagen summit.

Some people at senior level in the media – I saw this first-hand at the BBC and heard more through conversations with fellow reporters in the written press – had always had reservations about climate change. It is easy to understand why. Fossil fuels had turned the wheels of the global economy for more than a century, and now we were being asked to give them up. And for what? To avoid a set of impacts that might occur at some point in the future, probably in parts of the world far from London.

Scientists seemed unconvincing, insisting in one breath that 'the science is settled' and in the next being unable to say with any degree of precision what impacts would occur when, or to explain the apparent slowdown in global warming. The Stern Review was accused of having chosen a key parameter (the discount rate) in order to reach the conclusion that Gordon Brown wanted it to reach. The Americans under George W. Bush were sceptical about the need to reduce emissions, while the Chinese and Indians were building coal-fired power stations and buying cars like there was no tomorrow.

Renewable energy was expensive, while the oil companies that had brought the UK untold riches from the North Sea looked like remaining serious players forever. After taking us into war in Iraq through dogged adherence to the WMD narrative, Prime Minister Tony Blair did not seem so much the 'pretty straight sort of guy' he had once claimed to be, a view which touched the rest of the cabinet that supported him. Was the IPCC report just another dodgy dossier?

Part of an editor's job is to poke the consensus. As Ross Clark observed in 2018 in a *Spectator* article on ocean plastics: 'When public opinion is so much in agreement on an issue, we should all be on our guard.'[265] And to some, the consensus appeared too big, too convenient, too self-congratulatory, too smug – and down below, too full of holes – to be swallowed whole.

There was, too, another set of voices putting forward an alternative narrative – 'another side of the story' – that seemed both plausible and attractive. Blogs such as *ClimateAudit* were routinely running their rulers over mainstream climate science and claiming to find it wanting – in statistical techniques, in data, in the reliability of computer models and, therefore, in its conclusions.[266] Well before 2008, such bloggers were in contact with contrarians with influence – not least through the medium of Benny Peiser, GWPF director since its launch in 2009 but previously a sports sociologist at John Moores University in Liverpool. For years Peiser's CCNet had issued daily bulletins collating contrarian articles in media around the world, and numbered Parliamentarians on its mailing list.[267]

The real ace that this community held was that they appeared to be the 'little guys'. *ClimateAudit's* Steve McIntyre had spent his life in the minerals business and had become interested in climate change in retirement.[268] He was not the only questioner of the consensus apparently motivated by public-spirited concern that the establishment was deluding itself. GWPF played up the 'little guys' narrative, with Lord Turnbull writing in a foreword to one of its reports: 'We increasingly live in the world of Erin Brockovich versus Pacific Gas and Electric or David versus Goliath, where committed individuals with few resources can dig away at an issue.'[269]

What they said was intuitively appealing. Global warming appeared to have slowed down, or even stopped. Scientists had not predicted the slowdown and could not explain it, but these guys had a simple explanation: the scientists' computer models did not work, and politicians were not prepared to admit it was all a con because of the political capital they had invested.

This was a massively attractive narrative because, if they were right, we would not need a new United Nations agreement to combat climate change with all the regulation that might imply. We would not need a clean energy transition. Oil and gas companies could continue underpinning our pension schemes and contributing billions to national treasuries; we could stop building those subsidised and, to some, unsightly windmills. For those on the political Right, an additional bonus was that energy could go back to being entirely privately-owned and market-based. And those on the very far fringes of the Right also liked the idea that at least one issue would be taken out of the control of the United Nations and what they perceived as its drive for global government.

A truly sceptical eye would have noted that for a bunch of little guys, the contrarians had a lot of powerful friends and allies. Unlike Erin Brokovich or the Biblical David, GWPF could number seven members of the House of Lords among its public supporters. Contrarian MPs wrote to the BBC director-general demanding to know how many climate sceptics were being featured in its coverage. Channel Four broadcast *The Great Global Warming Swindle*.[270] National newspapers and websites gave prime real estate to a cohort of contrarian commentators including James Delingpole and Christopher Booker.

In 2009, Booker's *The Real Global Warming Disaster* received reviews in the *Telegraph*[271], *Express*[272], *Mail on Sunday*[273] and *Spectator*[274], by some of the UK's most garlanded columnists including Peter Hitchens and Simon Heffer. To get any book reviewed by such a phalanx of Tier 1 columnists is remarkable. All found it to their taste, none displaying one iota of the scepticism shown by the one mainstream media reviewer with a background in science, Philip Ball, who wrote in *The Observer* that while 'moved to a queer kind of admiration for the skill and energy with which Booker has assembled his polemic, much, including the central claim, is bunk.'[275]

Perhaps even more remarkable is that the *Express*, *Telegraph* and *Spectator* all advertised Booker's tome through their own book services at discounted prices.

For an argument that some claimed could not get heard, the downplaying and questioning of climate change seemed to be getting an awful lot of airtime.

I was never privy to editorial conversations at media organisations such as the *Spectator*, *Mail* and *Telegraph*. But the sense I had then, and which returns on re-reading articles from the time, is that repeated questioning of climate change by influential commentators, combined with lobbying operations by 'think-tanks' with influence on the political Right, had created an atmosphere in which the 'establishment' view of climate change as a real and potentially serious problem was seen as unsupportable and ripe for toppling.

And then, in 2009, came the release of the hacked UEA emails and the almost exactly coincident launch of GWPF.

No editor of a national newspaper can spend as much as one per cent of his or her time thinking about climate change and energy. There are far too many other stories, usually much more immediate, in politics, business, health, and crime. There are wars, celebrities and sports to cover. So, given that even specialist environment journalists had little spare capacity as the Copenhagen summit approached to examine the email trove critically, there was absolutely no chance of editors doing so on the timescale needed. Meanwhile, the story was moving on, driven by contrarian individuals and organisations, not least Lord Lawson who – with Benny Peiser at his side – called for an inquiry into these 'very serious allegations'.

In some newsrooms, the Copenhagen debacle served to confirm long-held doubts – showing that governments were not serious about solving climate change, perhaps because they had privately realised it was not a serious problem.

As 2010 began, so did the series of inquiries based on the email hack and, as a result of the erroneous claim on the melting of Himalayan glaciers, into the IPCC. Now, even the establishment appeared to be having second thoughts about the solidity of climate science.

The BBC was under the cosh from politically-connected contrarians, who demanded an inquiry into its coverage. Elsewhere, previously 'shy contrarians' flexed their muscles. One environment correspondent working in the national news media told me that his editor gave him the cold shoulder, apparently convinced that the correspondent had been suckered by scientists and become part of the 'conspiracy'. Reuters appointed a climate sceptic to a senior editorial post, from where he tried to get specialist correspondents to downgrade climate change and give more time to contrarian views.[276]

It was a surreal and schizoid time, because while all of these inquiries were taking place, climate science itself continued to function. New findings emerged on a weekly basis, and nothing challenged the basic picture of a planet where additional heat trapped by additional greenhouse gases was disrupting the natural world from the poles to the Equator. But in the parallel story, the processes and standards of climate science were under scrutiny like never before.

Personal stories abounded too, sometimes with a force that one rarely saw in science and environment reporting. One eminent US scientist needed a security guard when he attended a big scientific meeting in San Francisco, so specific and lurid had been the threats against his person. In an article that to many brought back memories of David Kelly, the scientist who committed suicide after being named as the source of a media story on Iraq's non-existent weapons of mass destruction,

UEA's Professor Phil Jones detailed how the weight of opprobrium had pushed him to contemplate ending his life.[277]

The white supremacist group Stormfront published a webpage detailing how many leading players in climate science and politics were Jewish.[278] I attained the honour of having a blog established just to attack me, Black's Whitewash[y] – an honour that as far as I know I share with only one other environment correspondent, Alister Doyle of Reuters. Alister's was slightly more menacing than mine, as the blogger concerned had a visible penchant for guns as well as climate denial.

However – smoke clears. One by one, the inquiries into the IPCC and UEA reported back. None of them found a smoking gun.

Newspapers that had smelled a rat over the perhaps-too-convenient 'consensus' did not all accept these conclusions. Christopher Booker complained about the various inquiries' panels, claiming in the *Sunday Telegraph* that 'almost all their members were committed, even fanatical advocates of global warming'.[279] Andrew Montford, proprietor of the contrarian BishopHill blog (and now GWPF's deputy director), compiled a report for GWPF claiming to have identified numerous problems with their work.[280]

However, some of the contrarians' claims fell down spectacularly as well. One was the charge that the Climatic Research Unit at UEA made it

---

[y] Now sadly defunct

impossible for independent researchers to download and process weather station data, so its temperature record could not be independently verified. The Muir Russell inquiry team asked one of its computer-literate researchers to locate weather station data, download it and compile a basic temperature record. It took two days.

And the emails? As one looked deeper, it became clear that a really important aspect of their launch was that spin had preceded content. As the contexts emerged for the parts of the emails that contrarian bloggers had chosen to highlight, it became evident that while there was substance in the charge that some scientists had tried to evade Freedom of Information rules in ways that they should not have done, there was no basis to the much more serious charge of a systematic attempt to distort climate science.

Much has been written about this elsewhere, and I do not plan to repeat it. One example will suffice: the email that Phil Jones wrote to a number of fellow scientists in which he reports: 'I've just completed Mike's *Nature* trick of adding in the real temps to each series for the last 20 years (ie from 1981 onwards) and from 1961 for Keith's to hide the decline'.

This, some claimed, showed that Jones had been trying to hide a decline – a fall – in the global temperature.[281] But closer inspection showed that the email was written in 1999, when the 'global warming hiatus' meme was not even in nappies. What the email actually referred to was a procedure – 'trick' is a term that scientists might use informally – to combine a temperature record from the age of thermometers with another record from a preceding period where temperatures had to be deduced from natural phenomena – in this case, the growth-rings of trees. Obviously the two lines need to be spliced together somehow. An attempt to hide a falling global temperature it emphatically was not.

The exact circumstances of the email hack and release have never been revealed, and presumably never will be. The Norfolk Constabulary launched a criminal inquiry but abandoned it three years later as various trails went cold.[282] They concluded that the emails had definitely been stolen, not leaked, and that the hack had been 'sophisticated and orchestrated'. Circumstantial evidence pointed variously to involvement of players in Russia, Saudi Arabia and the US, but no agent was ever conclusively identified.

For Phil Jones, the episode was nothing less than 'a concerted attempt to put a question mark over the science of climate change in the run-up to the Copenhagen talks'.[283] And an interesting tidbit emerged a couple of months later in the form of a comment from Steve Mosher, a software specialist with connections in contrarian circles, who was one of the first to see the email trove.[284] Contacted by – presumably – the purveyor of the stash, complaining that 'nothing was happening', Mosher had replied: 'A lot is happening behind the scenes. It is not being ignored. Much is being co-ordinated among major players and the media. Thank you very much.'

One can make of the term 'co-ordination' what one will.

The contrarians' demand for a review of BBC coverage, meanwhile, rebounded like a squash ball. The BBC Trust commissioned University College

London geneticist Professor Steve Jones, author of several popular science books and an occasional presenter of BBC radio programmes, to look across the whole of the BBC's science output including climate change and assess its accuracy and impartiality.[285]

Published in 2010, his report concluded that the BBC did a pretty good job of reporting science. On climate change, he came down rather markedly against the contrarians and their supporters within the BBC. 'For at least three years,' he wrote, 'the climate change deniers have been marginal to the scientific debate but somehow they continued to find a place on the airwaves. Their ability so to do suggests that an over-diligent search for due impartiality – or for a controversy – continue to hinder the objective reporting of a scientific story even when the internal statements of the BBC suggest that no controversy exists.'

In other words – the BBC was giving too much weight to contrarians, he concluded, not too little. The BBC Trust and management accepted the report in its entirety, bar one tweak to the job description of the new science editor.

Nevertheless; until about 2009-10, there was a case for arguing that much of the press's response to the UEA email hack and the Copenhagen debacle had been legitimate. Big questions of probity and competence had been asked, and it was entirely right that journalism should seek after truth in the same way that it would in any other sector of society. Scientists might complain – but there was no basis for making them immune from inquiry.

But there is also a case for arguing that this is the point at which some publications began to lose their way – the point at which Peter Oborne's charge against the right-leaning press begins to be justified.

Again, I am without the privilege of having gone to the editorial meetings – still less to the lunches where editors chink port glasses with weighty figures in Parliament and business. But an inescapable conclusion is that the arguments against the seriousness of climate change and the feasibility of a clean energy transition promulgated by Nigel Lawson, Christopher Booker and others, combined with the triple bombshell of the UEA hack, the Himalayas error and the Copenhagen failure, established a 'new normal' for the important newspapers of the Right. News correspondents would continue reporting on new science and political developments – but the papers' central view, reflected in the heartland of their comment pages, would be fundamentally sceptical.

Figures who had argued against the establishment view all along had, it seemed, been vindicated most dramatically. Now, who would argue against them continuing to be right? Who would question their assertions that the public hated wind power, or that poor Africans were being wrongly deprived of cheap coal? Which scientists would have the access that allowed them to show editors that the fundamentals of science had not after all been shaken to their core?

Proper scepticism involves being prepared to question your own views as well as those of others.

It means being prepared to admit when you have been shown to be wrong. It means being just as sceptical about the views of those with whom you instinctively sympathise as about those of a different camp. Ross Clark was entirely correct to say that, if a consensus appears too full and too easy, it should be probed. But if probing proves it to be broadly correct, there is no logic to continuing to act as though it were not. To do so is not scepticism, merely contrarianism-signalling.

But who was there now within an editor's earshot who would be sceptical about the sceptics?

One set of charges against contrarians concerns the manufacturing of attacks on climate science, the most infamous being that which its instigators dubbed 'AmazonGate'.

In the aftermath of the IPCC's faulty claim about the likely melting date for Himalayan glaciers, contrarian campaigners decided to go through the IPCC reports line by line, reference by reference and see if they could find any similar examples.

The veteran British campaigner Richard North homed in on a statement that about 40 per cent of the Amazon rainforest could 'react drastically' to a reduction in rainfall.[286] The hypothesis was that the risk of fires would rise as rainfall decreased, and at least some of the forest would probably be replaced by savannah. This would be significant globally: as one of the world's three biggest rainforest areas, the Amazon is a major absorber of carbon dioxide and generator of oxygen.

North found that the IPCC had sourced this passage from a report by environment group WWF – the same source as the report containing the erroneous claim on melting of Himalayan glaciers. This carried the heady whiff of another claim from a green campaign group being treated as though it were real science. North took it to the *Sunday Times*, whose environment editor Jonathan Leake phoned Professor Simon Lewis, an expert in tropical forests and climate change with posts at Leeds University and University College London, for his views.

Lewis gave Leake a long set of comments, concluding that the claim was justified by a number of scientific papers. As he told BBC News: 'The IPCC statement is basically correct but poorly written, and bizarrely referenced. It is very well known that in Amazonia, tropical forests exist when there is more than about 1.5 metres of rain a year, below that the system tends to "flip" to savannah.'[287]

The IPCC could and should have cited scientific papers, he said, rather than the WWF report – but science did support the '40 per cent at risk' conclusion, and the IPCC was right to include it. After writing his story, Leake phoned Lewis again and read the article to him, to make sure it reflected his views accurately – and Lewis said it did. Lewis also helped the newspaper compile a graphic to accompany the article showing how climate change would affect the Amazon.

The article that emerged was very different.[288] Under the headline 'UN climate panel shamed by bogus rainforest claim', it claimed that the IPCC statement 'was based on an unsubstantiated claim by green campaigners who had very little scientific expertise'. Whereas the initial version had quoted Simon Lewis saying the IPCC conclusion was sound, the published version said:

'Scientists such as Lewis are demanding that the IPCC ban the use of reports from pressure groups. They fear that environmental groups are bound to cherry-pick the scientific literature that confirms their beliefs and ignore the rest. It was exactly this process that lay behind the bogus claim that the Himalayan glaciers were likely to melt by 2035 – a suggestion that got into another WWF report and was then used by the IPCC.'

Thus Simon Lewis became, in the article's telling, the person who slated the IPCC claim as 'bogus'. The article still bore Jonathan Leake's byline, but at the bottom was the statement: 'Research by Richard North'.

Simon Lewis is more worldly than many scientists, and decided not to take this massive distortion lying down. He wrote a detailed rebuttal in the comments section beneath the article – which was deleted. He then wrote a letter to the *Sunday Times*, which the paper chose not to publish. Finally, he made an official complaint to the press regulator, the Press Complaints Commission (PCC), on which *The Guardian* reported.[289]

Eventually, the PCC brokered an agreement that saw the *Sunday Times* publish a long correction acknowledging that 'In fact, the IPCC's Amazon statement is supported by peer-reviewed scientific evidence'.[290] It acknowledged that one of the people it had labelled a 'green campaigner' was in reality an expert in forest management, and clarified that Simon Lewis did not believe that the IPCC should not use material from environment groups because of 'the prospect of those reports being biased in their conclusions'. The original article was removed from the *Times* website.

Perhaps the most interesting line of the correction was the last: 'A version of our article that had been checked with Dr Lewis underwent significant late editing and so did not give a fair or accurate account of his views on these points. We apologise for this.'

Corrections and retractions do not come more clear-cut than this one. Clearly, someone high up in the *Sunday Times* editorial team did not like the line taken by the journalist it was employing specifically to write on this subject – a correspondent of considerable experience and expertise – and decided it preferred the version offered by a campaigning blogger.

A look at Richard North's own blog output from the period is instructive. On 31 January, the day that the *Sunday Times* article saw publication, he wrote: 'The detail is familiar to readers of this blog, and some might note a small addition at the end of the piece which says: "Research by Richard North", in what has been a fruitful partnership.'[291]

On another post he was less than impressed by an article that appeared the same weekend in the *Sunday Telegraph*, in which Richard Gray and Rebecca Lefort reported that 16 WWF studies had been quoted in the IPCC report.[292,293] What provoked his ire was the fact that Gray and Lefort had contacted some of the scientists whose research WWF (and thus the IPCC) had cited. They reported that the scientists '...expressed surprise that their research was not cited directly, but said the IPCC had accurately represented their work.'

'Whaaaaaaaaaaa?' North writes (*sic*). 'What kind of hackwittery is this? Are they barking mad or just stupid?' After dismissing Gray and Lefort as 'children', he concludes: 'But hey, Richard Gray and Rebecca Lefort are *real* journalists. They are the professionals. So they ring up the authors of the *Nature* papers who tell them the IPCC "had accurately represented their work". And that's what goes in the newspaper, contradicting Booker and missing a front-page story.'

The reference to Christopher Booker is also instructive. Booker wrote in his column the same weekend: 'It is now six weeks since I launched an investigation, with my colleague Richard North, into the affairs of Dr Rajendra Pachauri, chairman of the UN's Intergovernmental Panel on Climate Change...'.[294] I do not know whether it qualifies as an 'investigation' or not, but certainly North was on Pachauri's tail, posting well over 50 blog entries critical of the IPCC chief in the single month of January 2010 alone.

To anyone who was involved in climate change at close quarters during this period – as journalist, scientist or campaigner – this episode is ancient history. Time has moved on. My reason for bringing it up is because I think it illustrates perfectly the knot into which British journalism tied itself on climate change.

There are two key facets. One is the extraordinarily close connection between North and Booker, which would see the latter apparently deploy absolutely no scepticism towards material generated by the former – someone who ought properly to have been regarded as a source, with all the need for scrutiny that implies.

The second is North's comment about Richard Gray and Rebecca Lefort. Intended to be dismissive, North actually loses the argument instantly. Yes – Gray and Lefort *are* the real journalists. The ones who do old-fashioned things like phoning people to check facts, who use scepticism on everything before them. And yet here is North arguing that the *Sunday Telegraph's* management should follow the *Sunday Times's* lead, and take the blogger and columnist more seriously than the professional reporters.

North's and Booker's apparent obsession with taking down Pachauri did eventually find its way into the newspaper. The conclusion, though, was a shot in the foot.

The *Sunday Telegraph* carried a story by the pair in which they related that shortly after the Copenhagen Summit, Viscount Christopher Monckton, a relative by marriage of Nigel Lawson's son Dominic and one of the UK's more colourful climate contrarians, had sent a letter to IPCC delegates demanding Pachauri's resignation because of 'conflicts of interest.' (The article appears to have been removed from the *Telegraph* website, but resides elsewhere on the World Wide Web.)

The way that Booker and North told it, Pachauri had 'established an astonishing worldwide portfolio of business interests with bodies which have been investing billions of dollars in organisations dependent on the IPCC's policy recommendations.' In short, he was 'accused of making a fortune' through business links to carbon trading companies that would be likely to increase in value if the IPCC made certain recommendations. The money Pachauri made from these businesses, Booker and North wrote, 'must run into millions of dollars.'

Which, given the febrility of climate change politics at the time, would have been a good story. However... an inquiry by KPMG concluded that there was no evidence for the allegations.[295] The *Telegraph* issued an apology; no damages were disclosed, but presumably the incident was not entirely free of costs for the newspaper.[296] Rajendra Pachauri continued as IPPC chair.

Once again, a 'real journalist' might have approached this from a neutral standpoint – might have made the calls, evaluated all the evidence and written a story that fully accorded with it. Instead, as with the *Sunday Times* on the Amazon, the *Sunday Telegraph* allowed itself to be carried along with the sound and fury rather than making sure that somewhere in the chain from source to printed page, someone was applying some scepticism – and paid a price, certainly in reputational terms.

Although the overall balance of media coverage on climate change has altered markedly since 2010 – more accurately, since about 2015, of which more anon – the problem of the columnist being given more weight than the expert continues.

Newspapers' opinion pages are in part an expression of what values the paper stands for. In part they are the place for insightful and appealing writing that can attract and retain readers. A third way of looking at it is that while news pages have an obligation to report the world as it is, opinion pages can paint the world as the editor or proprietor would like it to be. So it is that the

Sunday Telegraph could in that one single edition publish a news article and an opinion piece so obviously at odds with each other – the news story in which scientists back the IPCC's conclusions as sound and evidence-based, the opinion piece describing the IPCC as '... an institution now so discredited and scientifically corrupted that only those determined to shut their eyes could possibly defend it.'

There is no doubt that a number of editors and proprietors of some major UK newspapers were always suspicious of the 'climate consensus'. And effectively what a number of them did, now, was to out-source their opinion pages to a tiny group of writers who would consistently file articles that outlined the world as they would like it to be.

When you look at the contrarian commentariat in the UK media, three things strike you: how small it is, how tightly-knit it is, and how effectively it has penetrated some of the nation's most important newspapers.

The Times engages as a weekly columnist Matt Ridley, a member of GWPF's 'Academic Advisory Panel'. The *Sunday Times* carries a weekly column by Dominic Lawson, Nigel's son. The *Daily Telegraph* carries regular columns by its former editor Charles Moore, a GWPF trustee. All, of course, write about many more issues than climate change; but still, there we are.

The *Sunday Telegraph's* Christopher Booker has authored several reports for GWPF. The *Mail on Sunday* went down a slightly different track, engaging David Rose, the journalist who in the run-up to the invasion of Iraq probably did more than any other to popularise the notion that the regime possessed weapons of mass destruction and who confessed afterwards to having been 'bamboozled' by intelligence sources, as a special correspondent.[297] His periodic coverage of climate change and energy issues has included some bona fide 'exposés', for example on the environmental impacts of biomass power stations, but also hatchet jobs on the institutions of climate science. Rose has no formal GWPF affiliation, but has said he is 'proud to be friends' with the organisation.[298]

The *Daily Mail* and *The Sun* have opted not to engage a weekly contrarian columnist: the *Mail* will periodically commission Booker or *Breitbart News'* James Delingpole, the *Sun* Delingpole and, latterly, Ridley. Delingpole has no formal affiliation with GWPF but shows little scepticism about its reports.[299] Virtually all of the above turn up in *The Spectator*.

For anyone who cares about journalism, it is troubling to see the absolute lack of scepticism that editors display towards this tiny elite clique of commentators – especially, as we have seen, given the absolute reverse of scepticism that some commentators then deploy with both data and sources.

No publication has outsourced its climate change commentary with more abandon than *The Spectator*. It is a magazine with much to admire in the wit and edge of some of the writing: but there is precious little to admire in its climate change coverage, or the way it handles criticism.

In 2014, the IPCC published the second instalment

of its Fifth Assessment Report (AR5) – the instalment on Impacts, Adaptation and Vulnerability.[300] Shortly afterwards *The Spectator* ran a piece by Matt Ridley headlined 'We have a new climate change consensus – and it's good news everyone'.[301] The article's thesis was that the IPCC had concluded that humanity should adapt to climate change rather than try to stall it by reducing carbon emissions – with Ridley's opening sentence claiming it proved 'Nigel Lawson was right after all'.

Among the article's many problems, here is the big one: the IPCC had said nothing of the sort. As I noted earlier, there are very obviously limits to adaptation, and the IPCC's conclusion is that both adaptation and mitigation are needed. As the working group's co-chair Professor Chris Field told BBC News: 'The risk of severe and pervasive impacts goes up dramatically in a world that doesn't pay attention to high emissions.'[302] Ridley acknowledges the IPCC's position towards the end of the article – but by then the damage is done, given the headline, the standfirst, the opening sentence, the descriptions of adaptation and mitigation as 'alternatives' and of decarbonisation as 'futile'.

The merest glimpse at the Summary for Policymakers would have shown the reality of the IPCC's position. 'The overall risks of climate change impacts can be reduced by limiting the rate and magnitude of climate change, it says. 'Reducing climate change can also reduce the scale of adaptation that might be required... Since mitigation reduces the rate as well as the magnitude of warming, it also increases the time available for adaptation to a particular level of climate change, potentially by several decades... Greater rates and magnitude of climate change increase the likelihood of exceeding adaptation limits.'

One question, then, is how did *The Spectator* come to publish an article whose main thrust was so obviously at odds with the facts?

A clue to the answer came a week or so later. Two of the UK's foremost scientists involved in climate change, Professor Julia Slingo of the Met Office and Lord (John) Krebs who at the time chaired the Adaptation Sub-committee of the Committee on Climate Change, wrote a letter to the magazine pointing out the article's shortcomings.

They eventually received an email saying that Matt Ridley had seen the letter and had changed it: if Slingo and Krebs were happy with the new version, it would get published – if not, not. They were not happy, as the letter had been changed markedly, and so it was not published.

If staff on *The Spectator* had engaged in fact-checking themselves, they would have found inside five minutes the sentences from the IPCC report that I included above – and indeed many more in similar vein. Instead the magazine appears to have effectively outsourced adjudication on readers' comments – in a sense, had outsourced fact-checking – to the columnist who had put such a slant on reality in the first place.

The magazine did however print a letter from fellow columnist Hugo Rifkind:

> 'My colleague Matt Ridley is correct to note that in the press release which accompanied the IPCC's most recent publication, the word "adaptation" occurred 10 times, the word "mitigation" not at all.

> 'Possibly, this has something to with the fact that this was part two of a four-part report, and called "Impacts, Adaptation and Vulnerability". If Matt remains keen to learn what the IPCC feels about mitigation, he might be better off waiting for the press release on part three. Perhaps this won't mention it either, but I'd be surprised. It is to be called "Mitigation".'[303]

Ouch.

The Spectator's most spectacular piece of outsourcing came in 2015 during the first week of the Paris climate summit. The 5 December edition carried no fewer than six articles dismissing the summit and downplaying climate change.[304] Matt Ridley claimed that attempting to curb climate change is a 'conspiracy against the poor' and James Delingpole argued that people concerned about climate change have trouble with emotional connection. GWPF director Benny Peiser and GWPF trustee Charles Moore both assured us that the Paris summit would be a failure. Elsewhere there were attempts to take the mickey out of the UN climate process for sometimes holding summits in warm countries, and out of the BBC for having editorial standards. The edition carried not a single piece putting an opposing view on the summit or on climate change overall.

How such a thing can happen – how a magazine effectively gives its prime real estate over to a single set of opinions, and, one might argue, to a single organisation – is beyond my comprehension. But there it is.

A year or two later, after *The Spectator* published an

error-strewn James Delingpole article claiming that ocean acidification was essentially a made-up problem, I tweeted to its editor Fraser Nelson that the piece was flawed. His reply: 'What, some of the opinions are wrong?' No, I tweeted back – opinions are free, but in this case, some of the facts are wrong. I received no response.

This is perhaps strange given that *The Spectator* proudly proclaims that it 'upholds strict standards of accuracy'.[305] But Nelson's reply is, I think, indicative: in *Spectator*-world, expressing opinions vibrantly is more important than rooting them in reality. But on climate change, it appears, only one flavour of opinion is permissible.

And here we can start to put some flesh on the bones of Peter Oborne's charge that journalism on the Right has failed. At times, have editors and proprietors of *The Spectator, The Times* and *Sunday Times*, the *Daily Telegraph* and *Sunday Telegraph*, the *Daily Mail* and *Mail on Sunday*, and *The Sun* been, like him, 'too easily impressed' by this small but very well-connected group of self-proclaimed sceptics? Have their opinions been too convenient, their rhetoric too convincing, their connections too impressive?

One of the oddest aspects of the outsourcing is how far out of step these various opinions are with the public. Survey after survey reveals clear majorities in favour of curbing greenhouse gas emissions and adopting renewable energy.

In reality, I think, the point has never been to sway public opinion, but to impact politics. If you tell politicians repeatedly that wind farms are unpopular and expensive and that climate change is not a vote-winner, they may start to believe you – or perhaps to see it as politically expedient to take that stance. And there is probably no better way to tell them than through the opinion pages of Britain's most politically important newspapers. So it is that one will still hear MPs and peers claiming that onshore wind is unpopular or expensive, despite abundant evidence coming from their own government's research that neither is true.

A vignette emerged in the opinion survey that ECIU commissioned at launch in 2014.[306] Broadly consistent with the three-monthly surveys then done by the Department of Energy and Climate Change (DECC)[307], it found that 80 per cent of the British population supported renewable energy. But only five per cent knew that the public supported it; two-thirds of Britons estimated public support at under 50 per cent. A similar picture pertained on climate science, where only 11 per cent of the population knew the scale of the consensus among scientists that human greenhouse gas emissions are the major cause of current climate change.

The survey did not specifically examine the reasons for these mismatches; but it is inconceivable that misleading media coverage was not a major factor. Repeated claims that windfarms are 'detested', or whatever synonym you prefer, did not dent public support one iota – but they did shape the impressions that people, including politicians, held about public support.

And this is also where I rest my picture of an attempted coup – well, for a long while, an effective one – nothing less than the hijacking of the narrative by a tiny group of the political and media elite using a set of arguments that increasingly diverged from reality. Editors would be assured that wind turbines were unpopular when they were not. They would be told that climate change was the biggest scientific scandal of our time even as genuinely sceptical scientists showed the 'establishment' analysis had been right all along. They would be warned that energy policy was subjecting British industry to uniquely crippling prices, China and India had no interest in curtailing climate change, and the lights would go out within a few years. And as the editors were told, so were politicians and the public.

I am of course not talking of a coup of tanks and army barracks. But both that kind of coup and entirely political ones require control of the media. There is abundant evidence that the crucial importance of the media was acknowledged a long time ago in climate contrarian circles, both paid-for and conviction.

I am not saying that all contrarians act in bad faith; while some may, my impression is that others truly believe every word they write, and may genuinely think they are on a crucial mission to save the world from the 'cripplingly high' costs of a low-carbon transition. But that does not excuse the constant misrepresentations of public opinion or the one-eyed approach to climate science that have increasingly become contrarian stocks in trade ever since their real arguments began running out. It does not excuse the constant cherry-picking and dropping of caveats designed to make *a* piece of science look like *the* piece of science. It excuses neither the personal vilification nor the manufactured attacks exemplified by 'AmazonGate'.

You may of course argue with the word 'coup' if you like. But I for one am stumped for a better term.

4
Fake facts, cherry-picks and fantasies

Many climate contrarians, none more so than Nigel Lawson, present themselves as objective, impartial, sober, rational – taking positions dependent on an informed view of evidence. Sceptical, not doctrinal. And as I have shown, a decade ago it was entirely reasonable to take the positions they did, to pose tough questions to the orthodoxy. Those positions were not always based on all of the evidence, but almost always there was some evidence behind them.

Yet, to questions there are answers – answers that are now, increasingly, in. Was there a conspiracy within climate science? No. Is the Earth's biosphere warming? Yes. Is the advance of renewable energy leading to power cuts? No.

It would be heartening to be able to say that as the evidence changed over the last decade, the positions of people who term themselves 'sceptics' shifted accordingly. Unfortunately, it has not turned out this way.

In the real world, climate science, climate diplomacy and energy economics have moved a massive distance since 2008. Yet the UK's conviction contrarians continue to advance pretty much the same arguments as they did a decade ago. Tackling climate change will mean 'closing down virtually all our economy', wrote

Christopher Booker as recently as April 2018.[308] China plans to double its greenhouse gas emissions by 2030, he continued – ignoring evidence that its Paris Agreement pledge and national development plans imply an emissions rise of only about 10 per cent and perhaps nothing at all.[309]

In 2018, James Delingpole assured us that it would be a good thing if carbon emissions rose faster than expected 'because emissions are closely linked with economic growth – and economic growth makes us happy and richer and gives us the stuff that we want'.[310]

In 2017, Nigel Lawson told the BBC Today Programme audience that the global temperature had fallen over the last decade,[311] David Rose for the *Mail on Sunday* revisited the trope that climate science is a huge and expensive conspiracy,[312] and Matt Ridley assured us that an industry that hardly exists in the UK and in which few investors are interested, shale gas, would definitively provide energy 'at a cost well below that of renewables'.[313]

In 2018, contrarians can only seek to justify the majority of their positions by three approaches: say things that are simply untrue, cherry-pick findings from the smorgasbord of evidence that back their pre-existing narratives, or make absurdly confident claims on issues that are unknown and currently unknowable with precision. In this next section, I will run through some examples of each approach. Once again, there are some rabbit-holes and cul-de-sacs to be navigated. Although the examples are important in and of themselves, more important still are the thought processes underlying them.

Alternative realities

As an economist who supports the use of GDP growth as an indicator of economic well-being, and as the chair of an 'educational think-tank' on climate change policy, you might assume that Lord Lawson would be au fait with the evidence on how the UK was doing on both counts. So how to explain his claim on the BBC Today Programme in 2014 that tackling climate change would 'take us back to pre-industrial standards of living'?[314]

There is not, and never has been, a shred of evidence to back this idea. But in an era that has seen the UK advance economically at a G7-beating rate while also leading that bloc in the speed of emissions reductions, the claim is truly extraordinary. And the figures are out there for anyone to find. Still harder to explain his 2017 Today Programme claim that 'if anything, temperatures have gone down over the last decade' – a decade that saw three successive years post record-breaking warmth. This claim was so glaringly wrong that GWPF itself had to issue a correction.[315]

Charles Moore, the former *Daily Telegraph* editor and current GWPF trustee, showed a similar unfamiliarity with the fullness of the evidence in a June 2018 article for the *Telegraph*.[316] Praising Donald Trump for having pledged to leave the Paris Agreement – a pledge that he has yet to fulfil – Moore's central claim is that the US has reduced its carbon emissions more successfully than any other major nation, and done so through the simple medium of shale gas.

This is wrong in two fundamental ways. US greenhouse gas emissions are at almost exactly the same level as they were in 1990, having risen until 2005 and then declined again.[317] Over the same period, the

UK cut its emissions by 41 per cent.[318] The UK is streets ahead. If we start in the year that the US government generally prefers, 2005, the US has cut its carbon emissions more than the UK in absolute terms; in proportional terms, the UK again leads. And seeking to make the argument in absolute terms is highly specious: the US economy is six times bigger than the UK's, so of course a cut of a few percent will dwarf in absolute terms a much bigger percentage cut for the UK.

US emissions have fallen by 12 per cent since 2005, the UK's by 34 per cent. Across the G7, the US has performed not only worse than the UK, but also worse than France, Italy and Germany.[319]

The second issue is that shale gas has not been the only factor behind the fall in US emissions. In electricity generation, coal is being ousted by both gas *and* renewables – gas provided 32 per cent of generation in 2017, renewables 17 per cent.[320] Demand is also falling. The US Environmental Protection Agency puts it like this: 'Due to a general shift from a manufacturing-based economy to a service-based economy, as well as overall increases in efficiency, energy consumption and energy-related CO_2 emissions per dollar of gross domestic product (GDP) have both declined since 1990.'[321]

And the UK and all the other countries performing better than the US have, of course, cut their emissions entirely without shale gas.

Moore also gives a faulty picture on electricity prices. He claims that, in the US, the 'shale revolution' means that energy prices are falling. Government figures show the opposite – a *rise* in the retail electricity price of about 50 per cent since 2001.[322] Even more startling was a report in September 2018 by the US Energy Information Administration showing that a third of US households have trouble paying energy bills, with one-fifth – an estimated 25 million households – going without food, medicine or other essentials in order to do so.[323]

Moore's reading of the position of developing countries is also faulty. He writes: 'Poorer countries won't decarbonise unless richer ones pay them stupendous sums' – referring, presumably, to the sum of $100bn per year that richer nations promised, at the Copenhagen summit in 2009, to raise by 2020. This is misleading in two ways. First, the money is supposed to be used to help poor countries prepare for climate change impacts as well as to 'green' their economies. Secondly, the majority – just over 60 per cent – of the emission curbs that developing countries pledged to make at the Paris summit are not conditional on a transfer of money.[324]

A related and equally familiar argument holds that the interests of developing countries are best served by burning coal, often cited as the cheapest modern form of energy. It is said that the poorest nations really want to develop using coal as their staple power source – but western countries and western environmentalists are preventing them. In contrarian circles, this argument is probably most closely associated with Danish economist Bjorn Lomborg – but like all the others, it does the rounds. It is also one of the arguments that regularly rubs shoulders with paid advocacy programmes such as the Advanced Energy for Life PR campaign funded by Peabody Coal, founded on the somewhat head-scratching claim that 'Coal is key to human health and welfare along with a clean environment.'[325]

Any western environmental group would be startled to know it had the power to dictate the energy policy of a developing country – especially given that many developing countries are not exactly fond of western environmental groups. Literally dozens including Cambodia, Ethiopia, Egypt, The Philippines and Uganda have curtailed the activities of NGOs in the last five years.[326] It would be very strange indeed were these nations then to let such organisations dictate their energy policy.

If the argument is that western environmentalists are blocking coal through other mechanisms, such as by lobbying western governments and international finance organisations to stop supporting it – well, then here is a clear logical flaw, because another canonical contrarian argument is that these developing countries *are* building more coal-fired power stations and will continue doing so for years. It cannot be the case that they are both building them and simultaneously not building them.

Matt Ridley looked in on the coal and development issue in a *Times* column in 2015.[327] He notes, correctly, that a vast number of people in Africa lack access to modern forms of energy, which creates rising pressure to burn wood and charcoal. The solution, he argues, is to increase Africa's consumption of fossil fuels:

> 'Africa is awash with fossil fuels – but not the capital to build plants to turn them into electricity. Just to get sub-Saharan electricity consumption up to the

levels of South Africa or Bulgaria would mean adding about 1,000 gigawatts of capacity, the installation of which would cost at least £1 trillion.'

The reality of fossil fuels in Africa is rather different. According to the BP Statistical Review of World Energy, the continent possesses a mere 7.5 per cent of the world's known oil reserves and 7.1 per cent of its gas reserves.[328] They are concentrated in a handful of countries – Libya, Algeria, Egypt and Nigeria. All others would have to import gas were they to invest in gas-fired power stations. Of those four nations, only the last-named is in sub-Saharan Africa – and the oil industry in Nigeria's Ogoni Delta has emphatically not been a development, human rights and environmental success story given its history of toxic pollution and bloodshed which culminated in the murder of Ken Saro-Wiwa and his fellow activists in 1995.[329,330]

But the 'Africans need fossil fuels' argument usually points towards coal. And on coal, the reality is even more starkly at odds with the rhetoric. Few African countries have coal mines or even known coal reserves – only South Africa and Zimbabwe are among the world's top 35 coal-rich countries.[331] The BP Review notes that Africa overall has just 1.4 per cent of the world's known coal reserves.

1.4 per cent! 'Awash'???

Coal expansion would be a recipe for import dependence. And that is even if you assume that a mass coal-powering of Africa is possible, given limitations on roads, rail and already creaking electricity grids. One could argue that Africa's infrastructure is due an upgrade, and maybe so – but given the general antipathy of the climate contrarian community to overseas development aid, it is hard to believe that they would advocate western nations putting in the £1 trillion that Ridley says would be needed.

It was not western blockage of coal-fired power stations that encouraged 5.2 million Bangladeshi home-owners to install solar panels.[332] Neither did WWF, from its Swiss headquarters, make Samoa vow to run entirely on renewables by 2021;[333] nor yet did Greenpeace force India's Prime Minister Modi to launch his International Solar Alliance at the Paris climate summit.[334] Coal might still make a narrow kind of sense for some developing countries – but the realities of energy independence, infrastructure, pollution and now simple cost mean that renewables make sense for many more.

In 2014, the International Energy Agency (IEA) reported that where people in rural Africa are gaining access to electricity, more than two-thirds are doing so through 'mini-grid and off-grid systems', increasingly based on solar panels.[335] Africa may not be awash in fossil fuels, but it certainly is in sunlight.

Each autumn, GWPF hosts a lecture, often given by a former political figure. Contributors include former Australian Prime Minister Tony Abbott, former Czech President Václav Klaus, and currently under-scrutiny Australian cleric Cardinal George Pell.[336]

In 2014, it was the turn of Owen Paterson MP, fresh from his short stint in office as UK Environment Secretary.[337] His lecture's headline claim was that under energy policy as it stood, the inevitable advent of more and more renewable generation meant that at some point 'the lights will go out'. His essential remedy was to scrap the Climate Change Act as it requires the use of renewable energy. Which would have some logic to it, except – the Climate Change Act does *not* require renewable energy. It is scrupulously technology-neutral.[338]

The lecture did briefly acknowledge this – but then continued as though it had not, with Paterson saying towards its conclusion:

> 'What I have wanted to demonstrate to you this evening, is that it is possible to reduce emissions, while providing power. But what is stopping this program (*sic*)? Simply, the 2050 legally binding targets enshrined in the Climate Change Act.
>
> 'The 80 per cent decarbonisation strategy cannot be achieved: it is an all-or-nothing strategy which does not leave any openings for alternatives. It requires very specific technology, such as supposedly "zero carbon" wind farms, and electric vehicles.'

Nor was the Act's technological neutrality stressed, it seems, in conversations with the *Daily Telegraph*, leading to an editorial stating that '...the 2008 Climate Change Act, which all the major parties supported, tied Britain into the most stringent targets in the world for the reduction of fossil fuels and the expansion of renewables, such as wind farms.'[339]

The four-pronged 'alternative' energy policy that Paterson advanced – shale gas, demand management, combined heat and power and small modular nuclear reactors – is perfectly compatible with the Act. There is no conflict at all.

This was not the only issue with the speech. Decarbonising electricity means that 'costs to consumers will go up,' he said – presumably unaware that domestic electricity bills were falling even as levies on those bills funded wind turbines and solar panels. 'We will have to abolish natural gas in most of our homes,' he continued – 'our homes must become all-electric'. The end to fossil gas use is correct. The deduction that heating will inevitably become electrically-sourced is not, given that there are several other options for low-carbon heating, including low-carbon gas.[z]

Even as Owen Paterson was talking down the UK's electricity system, it emerged that his lecture had been initiated, if not written, by his brother-in-law. A journalist checked the meta-data on an advance copy of the speech that had been circulated to him, and found, in the 'author' box of the Word document, the name 'Matt Ridley'. It is not clear to what extent the lecture's issues originated with the latter and how much with the former. But it makes a neat segue to...

---

[z] The principal two are biomethane, and hydrogen produced using low-carbon methods

Extreme cherry-picks

I noted earlier that 'lukewarmery' is basically an exercise in cherry-picking; and it is worth looking into a few of Matt Ridley's claims, as case studies in how contrarians home in on and develop lukewarm arguments. I focus on Ridley here because of his profile, but he is only one exponent among several.

Matt Ridley is probably the UK's most prominent climate contrarian. He is a talented and successful science writer, a hereditary member of the House of Lords, a member of GWPF's 'Academic Advisory Panel', and commands a weekly column in *The Times* of London. He often casts himself as an advocate for science – and in his excoriations of the environment movement over genetically-modified crops, for example, he generally has science on his side.

In January 2013, Ridley penned an article for the *Wall Street Journal* on the theme of 'global greening' – the idea that the 'greenness' of the Earth's land surface is increasing, with vegetation becoming richer.[340] He based the article on a talk given a year previously by an American scientist, Dr Ranga Myneni.

As Myneni relates in his talk, a considerable body of evidence had been accumulating, principally from satellite observations, to show that the Earth's land was becoming more richly covered with vegetation. Myneni explains that this can be driven by various factors. In some cases, climate change has made an area warmer or wetter, facilitating plant growth. Elsewhere, growth is driven primarily by additional carbon dioxide in the air or nitrogen in the soil. Because Myneni's talk is posted online, it is straightforward to compare what he says with what Ridley writes about it.[341]

Myneni suggests that half of the greening can be attributed to conditions becoming warmer and wetter, 'and the other 50% is possibly due to fertilisation – maybe the increase in CO_2, nitrogen deposition, anthropogenic influences and so on.'[342] Note the caveat word 'possibly', and the attribution to CO_2 *or* nitrogen. Myneni goes on to caveat the findings further, saying explicitly that the attribution to fertilisation is 'somewhat speculative' and 'not on solid ground'.

However, in his WSJ article, Ridley writes that Myneni concluded that '...roughly 50 per cent *is* due to carbon dioxide fertilisation itself' – removing Myneni's mention of nitrogen, and ignoring his caution about the degree of certainty. Ridley's claim had a wider impact, with Rupert Murdoch, owner of the *Wall Street Journal* and *The Times*, issuing the caveat-free tweet 'World growing greener with increased carbon. Thirty years of satellite evidence. Forests growing faster and thicker.'[343]

Ridley returned to the subject in 2015 in a *Times* column whose standfirst claimed that 'evidence is growing that high CO_2 levels boost crops and nourish the oceans' – the 'oceans' mention being truly extraordinary given carbon dioxide's real impacts.[344] And in October 2016, 'global greening' was the central theme of his GWPF annual lecture, this time held in the august halls of the Royal Society, Britain's national science academy – a venue presumably hired to confer on the lecture a patina of scientific standing.[345]

By this point, Ranga Myneni and others in his international research network had formally published their findings in the journal *Nature Climate Change*, and their conclusion on the role of elevated carbon dioxide had become stronger.[346] Now, they reported, they believed it contributed 70 per cent of the observed greening. More remarkable than the scientific paper, though, was the media release accompanying it from Boston University, where Myneni works.[347] After relating the paper's main conclusions, it reads:

> 'The beneficial aspect of CO_2 fertilisation in promoting plant growth has been used by contrarians, notably Lord Ridley (hereditary peer in the UK House of Lords) and Mr Rupert Murdoch (owner of several news outlets), to argue against cuts in carbon emissions to mitigate climate change...
>
> '"The fallacy of the contrarian argument is two-fold. First, the many negative aspects of climate change, namely global warming, rising sea levels, melting glaciers and sea ice, more severe tropical storms, etc. are not acknowledged. Second, studies have shown that plants acclimatise, or adjust, to rising CO_2 concentration and the fertilisation effect diminishes over time," says co-author Dr Philippe Ciais.'

I do not think I have ever come across, before or since, such a passage in a media release. Decoded, it means 'you have drawn conclusions from our research before that could not be justified; please do not do so again'. It is a truly extraordinary intervention.

If the intention was to invite a more holistic approach from Ridley, it did not work. In his GWPF lecture, he accused Myneni and his colleagues of having delayed formal publication of their paper so that it could not be incorporated into the IPCC's Fifth Assessment Report – an extraordinary claim, utterly at odds with the natural inclination of scientists, which is to want to see their work reflected in major global reports, and one that brought an angry retort from Myneni.[348]

All else aside, global greening is probably a 'good thing'. But the observations analysed by Myneni are only part of the evidence. Field experiments show that in many cases, higher levels of carbon dioxide in the air do result in more plant growth. Logically this ought to ameliorate climate change to some extent, with plants absorbing more carbon dioxide from the air. Indeed, research suggests this is already happening, with the size of the 'terrestrial carbon sink' – the amount of CO_2 drawn down from the atmosphere into land – approximately doubling in the second half of the twentieth century.[349] However, there is also evidence that this increase in CO_2 absorption has slowed down and may be coming to an end.[350]

In the context of crops, experiments also show that the CO_2 fertilisation effect can be short-lived, petering out in a few years. Climate change is forecast overall to reduce crop yields.[351] Another issue is that for one of the world's truly necessary foods, rice, increasing atmospheric CO_2 drives a decline in nutritional content, with grains becoming depleted in protein, zinc, iron and four types of Vitamin B.[352]

What the 'global greening' issue does very neatly is to illustrate the thought processes necessary to make 'lukewarmery' work. First, take something with a kernel of truth to it that fits your pre-existing narrative:

lukewarmery is after all based in science – just not in all the science. Secondly, ignore evidence, caveats or context that run counter to it, or might constitute a challenge. Thirdly, inflate the implication of your selected evidence way beyond that which it actually merits.

Two other aspects of the global greening story also shed light on how contrarianism maintains itself.

The first is the ability to abhor something in principle, but accept it when it supports your argument. One of the basic tenets of climate contrarianism is that computer models are not reliable. Well, as Ranga Myneni's team relates at the very start of their paper:

> 'Here we use three long-term satellite leaf area index (LAI) records and ten global ecosystem models to investigate four key drivers of LAI trends during 1982–2009... Factorial simulations with multiple global ecosystem models suggest that CO_2 fertilisation effects explain 70% of the observed greening trend...'

These particular computer models are apparently immune from the general criticism of unreliability because they produce evidence supportive of the favoured theory.

The other illustrative aspect is the belief that this is an unjustly side-lined story – a 'contrary view' that has either been ignored or crushed beneath the juggernaut of 'consensus'. Thus, when *The Spectator* carried an article based on Ridley's GWPF lecture, the headline claimed: 'The world is getting greener. Why does no-one want to know?'[353] The answer Ridley gives in the article is, as you might predict, that the 'climate change lobby' does not want you to hear about it. In reality, the phrase has been used and the phenomenon studied for at least a decade.[354]

The danger of picking specific bits of research and over-egging their significance was demonstrated when another scientific paper emerged in May 2018. This group of researchers looked again at the expansion of forests, and concluded that it has nothing to do with increasing carbon dioxide concentrations.[355] Instead, they found, it is principally due to land management improving as societies become wealthier and protect their forests – something that is not factored into the computer models used in the Myneni paper.

Their conclusion: 'We falsified the hypothesis that forest resources of the world expand because forest ecosystems respond primarily to environmental changes...'

Whether improved land management or rising CO_2 concentrations become accepted as the main driver of greening we will discover in years to come. Certainly, all scientists live with the knowledge that new research may overturn their favoured theory. So should commentators who profess to value science.

Global greening is far from being the only example of 'select-ignore-inflate' methodology in action. Earlier this year, during a debate in the House of Lords, Ridley asked government minister Lord Henley whether he was aware that '...the consensus among climate economists and, indeed, in the Intergovernmental Panel on Climate Change, is that the economic impacts will be positive for the next 40 or 50 years'.[356]

Almost certainly Lord Henley was not aware – for

the simple reason that this is not the 'consensus' among climate economists. As I showed in Chapter 2, the main aspect of the consensus, as encapsulated in the IPCC assessments, is that the economics are really hard to determine; there is a lot more confidence about the limitations of economics to make a firm analysis than there is about the analysis itself.

Had Ridley used an IPCC report as the basis for his claim, that would have exemplified the same 'criticism suspension' that I described with the endorsement of models in the global greening story: the contrarian view is generally that the IPCC is unsound, so quoting one of its conclusions with approval would be somewhat ironic. Nevertheless, it would have had some validity given that the IPCC is the organisation with the best claim to represent the consensus.

But, Ridley revealed, he was not quoting the IPCC[357] – instead the source was a new academic paper by Sussex University economist Professor Richard Tol.[358] The paper is a meta-analysis – taking a number of existing studies and drawing them together to paint, in theory, a more robust picture.

To take any single paper, even a meta-analysis, as the 'consensus' is a dangerous approach. Worse; even if we accept Ridley's definition of the 'consensus', his position quickly falls apart. Tol's paper is as carefully caveated as the IPCC assessment: '...it is unclear whether climate change will lead to a net welfare gain or loss...' '...estimates of the marginal impact of climate change vary so widely that the initial carbon price is more a matter of politics than economics...' '...estimates of the impact of climate change are incomplete...'

Ridley mentioned none of this caveating in his

question to Lord Henley. And although he knew that Tol's most fundamental statement was also caveated – 'the initial impacts of climate change *may well be* positive'[359] – the caveat had disappeared in his Lords intervention, which read 'the economic impacts of climate change *will* be positive'.

Tol goes on to make the point that carbon emissions to date may well already have ensured that global warming will pass the point (1.7°C) where, according to his analysis, impacts turn economically negative. Accordingly he argues the case for restraining carbon emissions – which Ridley completely ignores.

As an exercise in first picking the cherry and then then over-ripening it, this is hard to top.

Contrarian discussion of energy policy also yields a regular basket of carefully picked cherries, though perhaps they do not glisten quite as spectacularly as those in the climate change field.

The four energy costs that matter most are domestic electricity, domestic gas, industrial electricity and industrial gas. For domestic consumers, the UK sits near the European average for both gas and electricity prices.[360] British businesses enjoy some of the cheapest gas in Europe.[361] Only for industrial electricity prices does the UK sit near the top of the table, although even here the last few years have brought relief for the biggest consumers who now receive almost total exemption from 'green levies'.[362] Nevertheless, the narrative has been kept alive that British energy bills are high, becoming such a political issue that in the name of social justice, the government is to impose a price cap... for domestic consumers.

The first point here is that what people pay is a *bill*, not a *price*. Outside the world of electricity traders, very few people know or care what a unit of electricity costs; what they do know and care about is their bill. And bills are affected by many things other than the unit cost – particularly by the amount of energy wasted. A poorly-insulated house or a rickety piece of factory machinery will need much more energy to do the same job than a state-of-the-art equivalent.

As I noted in the previous paragraph, contrary to received wisdom and the narrative of 'cripplingly' high prices, UK energy bills have, on average, fallen over the last decade.[363] Part of the story is energy efficiency improvements funded by 'green levies' on energy bills.

Commentators who want to maintain the narrative that 'green levies cost the consumer', therefore, rarely refer to bills; almost always, only to prices. After the Committee on Climate Change produced a report in 2017 on 'Energy Prices and Bills', Centre for Policy Studies Fellow Rupert Darwall penned a critique in the *Daily Telegraph* that ignored the report's conclusions on falling bills entirely, not mentioning the B-word word once.[364]

A second energy price cherry-pick is to select a base year that serves to makes the desired point. (If this tactic seems familiar, it should, being exactly that used to launch the 'global warming pause' narrative through the selection of El Niño-boosted 1998 as the starting year.) Thus the 2016 report on the Economics of UK Energy Policy by the House of Lords Economic Affairs Committee, on which GWPF trustee Lord Turnbull sits, began with the assertion: 'The average domestic electricity bill was 58 per cent higher in 2016 than it was in 2003.'[365]

It is a big number, in and of itself correct. But when you look more closely, electricity prices in 2003 were unusually low. And if you start your analysis in a year of unusually low prices, you are more likely to see them rise. Professor Dieter Helm, the initial witness for that committee inquiry (who, to be clear, is on record as seeing climate change as a threat[366]) used the same misleading approach in his 2017 government-commissioned review of energy costs, starting his graphs in the unrepresentatively low-cost year of 2004.[367]

Interestingly, if you divide this period into two – the first 2003-2008, the second 2008-2018 – a different picture emerges. In the first period, energy prices and bills rose rapidly. In the second, unit prices rose slightly, but bills went down. And the sharp 2003-8 increase had nothing to do with government policies, instead being driven by the rebound of the wholesale price of gas from an artificial low.[368]

The gas market is an international market virtually free of government intervention. Therefore the rise in prices, which the committee attempted to pin on government policy interventions, had absolutely nothing to do with policy – unless you choose to view the 1990s decision, led by Lord Lawson as Energy Minister, to place the gas supply entirely in the private sector as the problematic 'intervention'. Which the committee most emphatically did not.

To be clear: 'green levies' do exert an upwards influence on bills, and this is set to continue. But as 'green levies' fund ever-cheaper renewable generation, the incremental cost of adding them is dwindling and will soon disappear – indeed, for onshore wind it has already disappeared. If levies continue to fund improvements in energy efficiency, bills will fall further. Meanwhile, the wholesale cost of free market-delivered gas remains the biggest single factor determining how bills fluctuate from one year to the next.[369]

So, to put all of this in one place: pursuing a narrative that 'green' policies are delivering energy costs that are some combination of 'cripplingly high', 'the highest in Europe' and 'rising', you need to look at the various cherries in your basket and pick out a suitable combination of:

- Referring only to electricity and to business consumers – not to gas, nor to households
- Referring only to unit prices, not to bills
- Selecting a baseline year that gives the trend that you want
- Ignoring what actually drove prices upwards in the period you selected.

Fantasy solutions

The real world is achieving significant progress in curbing emissions principally through two routes. The most effective one so far is by improving the efficiency with which we use energy.[370] The second is by reducing the amount of coal burned to generate electricity, replacing it with natural gas and renewables.

Logic would suggest that these trends will continue.

And indeed they are continuing, with a progressively greater proportion of investment in electricity generation worldwide going into renewables each year (70% in 2017).[371]

This presents a challenge for many contrarians, for whom renewable energy is canonically expensive, unreliable and unpopular. Therefore, a different future must be proposed.

Some argue for a future based on gas-powered generation. They are abetted in this by the UK government's unfortunate habit of referring to gas as a 'clean' fuel, when of course it is only 'clean' compared with coal and oil. And the UK cannot reduce carbon emissions much further through a coal-to-gas transition, given that coal already generates less than 10 per cent of our electricity and will be phased out fully by 2025.[372] The government should know better because the decarbonisation pathway it has mapped out suggests that in 2032 – in just 14 years' time – we will obtain only 15 per cent of our electricity from gas.[373] So, gas generation is not a long-term thing.

But that 15 per cent figure is not one that contrarians generally acknowledge. Thus it is, for example, that the Centre for Policy Studies think-tank could argue in 2016 that Britain should re-vamp its renewables policy and instead invest in new gas-fired power stations.[374] Its bulletin is a classic example of how the canonical contrarian arguments tessellate; the report prominently contends, not least in its title, that 'the lights will go out' in the near future, and deals with the climate-warming impact of new gas-fired power stations by the simple expedient of ignoring it.

But the approach seen most often is to seize on a

technology that is either unproven or does not exist, and promote it as better than renewables. The two favoured fantasy 'solutions' are shale gas and small modular nuclear reactors (SMRs), though others such as nuclear fusion occasionally gain a place at the table.

Given that shale oil and gas extracted in the US is very much a reality – one potent enough to re-shape international markets and geopolitics – I need to justify use of the word 'fantasy'. I do not mean that no shale gas will ever be extracted in the UK; in fact, at the time of writing it seems likely that some will be. What I mean is that as things stand, there is no evidence that a UK shale gas industry will turn out to be anything more than a bit-part player. It will depend ultimately on the opinion of investors. And in the real world, to base energy policy on something that does not exist, given the necessity of keeping homes and business provided with real therms and electrons rather than rhetorical ones, would truly be fantastic.

The British public opposes shale gas extraction, to an increasing extent. In the April 2018 edition of the government's quarterly survey, 32 per cent opposed and 18 per cent supported it – a turnaround from 2014, when more people supported it than opposed.[375]

The British public are wonderfully bloody-minded about intrusion into their communities. From Balcombe to Kirby Misperton, people are prepared to lie in the way of bulldozers and scale drilling rigs in order to stop shale gas operations taking place – in addition to using the full range of planning and licencing procedures at their disposal. Civil disobedience against shale gas is a reality, for whatever reason – and that alone may stop the industry in its tracks. There are technical concerns too. The UK's geology is not the same as in the US. Therefore the costs of extracting shale gas in the UK are unknown. Population density is much higher than in the US, and ownership of the rock beneath our feet different too. The UK's shale gas supporters may have their eyes fixed firmly across the Atlantic. But in Europe, several governments have banned it – where they have not, companies have abandoned their plans because they do not see the economics stacking up. Nowhere in Europe is shale gas extraction a reality; and although Britain might turn out to be the exception, it is hard to think of a single reason why.

A British shale gas industry would enhance our energy security, we are told. This is a somewhat odd contention, given that the gas would not be owned by Britain but by the company that extracted it. It would be fed into the national gas pipeline network and could then be distributed anywhere in Europe – perhaps further afield.

The energy security argument also misses another fundamental point. Investors in gas can basically put their money into four things: UK shale production, pipelines, storage or terminals for importing liquified natural gas (LNG). Were it to occur, burgeoning UK shale gas production would compromise the investment case for pipelines, storage and LNG terminals – each of which could fill a gas security need just as effectively.

There is too the rather obvious point that shale gas is just – well – gas. Generating electricity requires burning it in a power station. A vibrant UK shale gas industry would not on its own 'keep the lights on'. As I noted earlier, within 14 years we will be using gas for only about 15 per cent of our electricity, unless carbon capture and storage becomes a reality... so as a 'solution' to power sector decarbonisation, shale gas can make only a fractional contribution.

It could have a bigger role in home heating, industry, and powering heavy lorries and ships, giving companies about an additional decade's stay of execution. But given the abundance of LNG available on the ship-borne global market, there is no guarantee that UK shale gas will ever attract enough investment to blossom, for whatever end use.

Finally, is shale gas really 'low-carbon' compared with imported gas? Analyses vary. One conducted for the UK government in 2013 suggests that its carbon footprint is slightly lower than that of LNG.[376] However, a recent Dutch study indicates the reverse.[377] Either way round, the difference is marginal. What is certain is that shale gas rhetoric and lobbying can emphatically be high-carbon if it results in a slowdown in the rollout of genuinely low-carbon forms of energy.[378]

These points are almost entirely absent from the discourse of contrarian commentators. Claims vary from the optimistic to the extraordinary:

- From Matt Ridley in the House of Lords:[379] 'America has cut its carbon emissions by far more than we have, almost entirely because of shale gas displacing coal. By pursuing a strategy that encouraged unabated gas, we could halve emissions and cut bills at the same time.'
- From James Delingpole in *The Sun*:[380] 'Imagine if our new Prime Minister Theresa May could wave her wand and achieve the following miracles within

five years. Create 500,000 new jobs, slash our electricity bills, restore British manufacturing, boost our economy, make us richer and stop our energy supplies being held to ransom by Putin, the Arabs, the French and other foreign regimes. Well, the good news is she can, right now, and doesn't need magic to do it. All she needs to do is get fracking.'

- From Ridley in *The Times*, again phrased as though shale gas were an electricity generating technology:[381] '...the Bowland Shale beneath northern England holds one of the richest gas resources known: a huge store of energy at a cost well below that of renewables and nuclear.'
- From a *Spectator* editorial:[382] 'Not since the discovery of North Sea oil has the country had such an incredible opportunity.'

Having predicted in the past that thousands of shale gas wells would spring up across the nation, the latest government forecast is just 155 by 2025. Despite advocates' calls for yet more incentives for the industry, companies can bid right now to explore and extract. But overwhelmingly they are not interested. That is the free market reality.

The second favoured fantasy solution is the small modular nuclear reactor (SMR). Various companies have proposed different designs, but in ballpark terms each SMR would be at the very most one-third the size, and perhaps a lot less, of the giant reactors due to be constructed for the new Hinkley Point C nuclear power station, which are each rated at 1630MW. I use the adjective 'fantasy' here in exactly the same sense as with shale gas.

The theory goes like this. Hinkley-style reactors are proving too big, too complicated, too costly. Each power station requires such huge levels of up-front investment that few will ever be built. Building few of them means there is very little learning-by-doing, which in all areas of engineering tends to improve efficiency and safety and reduce costs.

By contrast, each small modular reactor would cost a lot less and be much faster to build. Potentially they could be built in factories and taken to operating sites completely or partially assembled. Operators could get their first SMR working, earn money from it, and use that income to construct the second, so reducing the up-front investment need. Reactors could either be distributed around the UK or clustered together on fewer, larger sites. Building more of them would improve the product and bring down the price.

All of this may turn out to be true. But equally there are reasons to believe it may not.

First, there have always been SMRs. Shippingport, the first commercial nuclear power station in the US, used a 60MW reactor that had been destined for an aircraft carrier.[383] The UK's first nuclear power station at Calder Hall also featured 60MW reactors.[384] Aircraft carriers and submarines still use reactors delivering tens or low hundreds of megawatts. They are almost all pressurised water reactors (PWRs) – the type which Rolls-Royce, the most voluble of the UK's would-be SMR builders, now proposes rolling out for power generation.[385] History shows that companies built larger reactors because that improved the economics. Quite why the economics should improve by now building smaller ones is not clear. And the fact that even industrial behemoths with excellent links to government such as Rolls-Royce are not going ahead suggests that they are not convinced themselves that the economics stack up against the renewables-based smart grid.

There is, too, the fact that the UK, like most other nuclear nations, has not solved its waste problem.

So, SMRs might or might not turn out to be a reality. If they are basically replicas of past designs, presumably they will work fine, but may turn out to be uneconomic compared to larger models. If they are new advanced designs – and some of the new proposed models do offer safety and waste advantages over PWRs – then presumably development, testing and licencing will take many years, and we have no idea about the likely cost.

As none are currently being built or even seriously developed, it is hard to tell; but history is not encouraging. Mike Shellenberger, the US pro-nuclear environmentalist and co-author of *An Ecomodernist Manifesto*, points out that innovation has made nuclear power more rather than less expensive.[386]

Despite support from pro-free market commentators, it is hard to envisage SMRs being built without state intervention. And as even the most derivative models would take at least 10 years to develop, licence and bring into operation, they cannot be a serious near-term 'solution' for the UK power sector given its 14-year timeframe for bringing emissions close to zero. Thereafter, the UK and other countries will need to increase generating capacity in order to power electric transportation and possibly heating, which is surely a more realistic timeframe for

SMRs. But for now, as Shellenberger drily notes: 'A design is not a power plant'.

If the economic viability of SMRs is unknown, so is their public acceptability. Although Owen Paterson's proposal that SMRs be 'installed near urban areas' to provide hot water as well as electricity has a certain logic to it, one does wonder quite how that will go down with communities that shudder at the thought of a shale gas well or a waste incinerator.[387]

Britain's contrarian commentators are not generally as hagiographic about SMRs as they are about shale gas. Nevertheless, the results of a 2018 survey of MPs are instructive, in terms of how discourse has been skewed.[388] Only 8 per cent knew that the cheapest way to add new electricity generation capacity in the UK is onshore wind. The same number thought that SMRs were the cheapest. Not a bad PR outcome for a product that does not actually exist.

It is, of course, worth drilling some exploratory shale gas wells and supporting research and development work on SMRs – and most definitely supporting nuclear fusion research, which, alone among energy 'super-technologies' has the potential to deliver something truly revolutionary. But we cannot rely on any of them to deliver clean energy more reliably and cheaply than is being delivered already by tried-and-tested alternatives of energy efficiency, renewable generation, demand shifting and, increasingly, the other components of the smart grid. Certainly not on the timescale indicated by climate science and the pathway needed to meet the UK's legally-binding emissions targets.

The three patterns I have outlined above – the use of

'fake facts', the picking of extreme cherries and the advocacy of unrealistic energy 'solutions' – undermine the useful work that the contrarian community has done in the past. And, on occasion, which it still does. Owen Paterson's GWPF lecture, for example, was constructive in its advocacy of energy efficiency, demand-shifting and combined heat and power (CHP) to save money, carbon emissions and cost.

On the vexed matter of biomass energy, contrarians (notably David Rose) have regularly highlighted the difficult questions raised by mass transport of wood from the US for burning in Britain's power stations. Genuine scepticism has a fundamental role to play in the very real debates around energy and climate change. But influence and credibility is lost through cleaving to arguments that are manifestly unsupportable.

There is much, too, about the climate contrarian movement that is deeply inconsistent. The most obvious concerns optimism and pessimism. Matt Ridley, for example, claims to be a 'rational optimist'.[aa] And his articles and speeches are full of optimism – sometimes rational, sometimes not – on everything, seemingly, apart from renewable energy. On this topic, which in the real world yields much to be optimistic about, he turns into a pessimist – costs will rise, the lights will go out, etc.

A related Ridley trope is that we should trust to the tremendous power of human ingenuity and innovation.

[aa] The title of his 2010 book

Yet his writings on energy are infused with a belief that human ingenuity and innovation will not be able to devise an energy system that makes increasing use of variable generation at ever-lower cost – even though this is already happening in the real world.

Another inconsistency surrounds the approach to state intervention and subsidies. Generally, contrarian commentators abhor them, advocating a free-market approach to energy. But in advocating support for bringing SMRs to market or for greater use of CHP, what are they backing if not state intervention and subsidies?

A third inconsistency surrounds energy developments in the countryside and local democracy. When communities protest against wind power, they are described in terms such as 'local people standing up for their rights against the blight of wind turbines across the countryside'. When they object to a shale gas well, they are 'green nimbies' whose rights to block development should be taken away.

You cannot have it both ways. You cannot be optimistic about human ingenuity and yet simultaneously pessimistic about a field where the application of human ingenuity is already yielding tangible success. You cannot support subsidies for technologies that do not and may never exist while resisting support for those that already make a real contribution – especially when the need for subsidies is disappearing as a result of investment in those technologies. You cannot congratulate plucky local communities for fighting against wind power companies and castigate them for doing the same against shale gas.

At least, you cannot do it constantly and expect people not to pick up the inconsistencies.

Above all, you cannot claim to be rationally and soberly sceptical and then repeatedly advance arguments based on error-strewn analysis, extreme cherry-picking and as-yet-non-existent technologies. People tend to notice that, too.

5
The costs of it all

Does the British media's love affair with the climate contrarian elite matter?

Well – if journalism is of value, of course it matters. News media is still the main route through which we, the public, gain our understanding of the world. With subjects that are complex and nuanced, we are additionally reliant.

Climate change is undoubtedly complex and nuanced. Responding to it is basically an exercise in risk management. Scientists do not (and never will) possess diagnostic or prognostic tools equivalent in precision to those of a medical specialist. Science is never going to be able to predict that in 2071, the sea level at Clacton-on-Sea will be precisely 42cm higher than it is now, or that the North Pole's first ice-free summer will occur in 2039.

What science has done, fitfully since 1824 when Joseph Fourier deduced that the atmosphere keeps the Earth warm and systematically since the establishment of the IPCC in 1988, is to map out the range of risks ahead. And then the choice before society, most obviously before political leaders, is to decide how to treat those risks.

If news media, or large chunks of it, are giving a systematically distorted picture of the risks of climate change – or of the feasibility and costs of clean energy – it is pretty obvious what impact that will have, given the critically important place of news media as providers of information and interpretation. In a democracy, absolutely it matters.

As well as distortions on the issues I covered in Chapters 2 and 5, a couple of other aspects of contrarianism stand out. One is the raising of doubt. After all, to convince someone not to do something, you do not necessarily have to persuade them that there is no problem – giving arguments as to why there might not be a problem can be enough. And on this topic, the sheer complexity of climate science, international climate politics and energy systems helps raise doubts. Although the overall picture of climate change and the energy transition is clear, for just about every trend in the world you can find an example that runs counter. Whataboutery flourishes:

- 'Glaciers are melting away all over the world and Arctic sea-ice shrinking? Ah, but what about Antarctic ice – isn't that growing?'
- 'The ocean's becoming more acidic? Ah, but it used to be much more acidic 100 million years ago.'
- 'Electric cars will reduce air pollution? Ah, but what about the one that caught fire the other day?'

Unless you are immersed in the details, the effect of these whatabouteries is to make the situation seem unproven – not so serious, or at least, perhaps not so serious.

The other tack that has proven very successful for contrarians is the appropriation of words such as 'rational', 'cool-headed', 'reason' and 'pragmatic'. Who would not agree with policy ideas to which that set of adjectives can be appended? Contrarians have generally been much more successful at this than their opponents in the environmental movement.

Nevertheless: at surface level, despite their long dominance over the media narrative, the contrarian elite have had very little influence on the overall shape of UK climate change policy. The Climate Change Act remains intact and very much alive; internationally, the UK remains a 'high-ambition nation' and actively engages in diplomacy and capacity-building in the developing world. It is one of the few developed countries living up to the pledge that all made in 1970 to spend 0.7 per cent of their GDP on overseas aid, and a fair chunk of that money now goes to climate change-relevant projects.[389]

One suspects – though it is impossible to prove – that in strictly climate change terms, the main impact of the UK's conviction contrarianism lies outside the nation's shores. It seems inconceivable that the *Wall Street Journal*'s reprints of sceptical *Times* articles has not given 'intellectual' backing to the US's own batch of high-carbon campaigners. Inconceivable also that visits from UK contrarians such as Viscount Christopher Monckton did nothing to shore up Australia's anti-climate change policies under the premierships of John Howard and Tony Abbott. How seriously contrarian articles in UK papers were treated in capitals in Africa and the Caribbean is a bigger unknown, and will probably remain so – though instinct suggests there has probably been some effect.

In the UK, the main impact has been on various

elements of energy policy. This is of course highly relevant to climate change, because it is energy policy – alongside, now, policies on transport, housing, farming, the countryside, industry and waste – that determine how far and how quickly carbon emissions are tackled.

It seems highly unlikely that a decade of newspaper columns disputing science and querying the feasibility of transitioning from fossil fuels had nothing to do with George Osborne's 2016 decision as Chancellor to scrap the Zero Carbon Homes policy at the last minute – an absolute no-brainer of a policy towards which the building industry had been working for nine years, which would have led to warmer homes and lower energy bills as well as curbing carbon emissions.

Contrarian pressure, particularly banner headlines and scandalised columns proclaiming how much Britons 'detest' wind turbines, certainly contributed to ministers virtually banning onshore wind power. Now that this is the nation's cheapest form of new electricity generation, not building onshore wind will put energy bills up.[390] It seems highly likely too that bellyaching about cost led to a decade of shilly-shallying on carbon capture and storage, a technology that just about every analysis concludes is necessary to curtail emissions from industry.

So far, so largely anecdotal. But there are at least two instances where contrarian pressure certainly contributed to policymaking that exerts an upwards push on energy bills. One is the undermining of energy efficiency policy – the second lies in the flood of baseless claims that the lights were in danger of going out.

A few years back, a strange thing happened in *The*

Sun: it simultaneously campaigned both for lower *and* higher energy bills.[391]

On the one hand, it had a People Power campaign. As of October 2014, 'nearly 15,000 people have joined... to cut up to £300 off energy bills.' On the other hand, it was also advocating against an update of EU regulations known as EcoDesign that would save money by saving energy, its rationale being the interpretation that 'Meddling EU chiefs are targeting the Sunday roast in their latest bid to make us save energy'.

Those EU bounders! How dare they cut our energy bills?

The Sun's line on the forthcoming EcoDesign update was reflected in the *Express*, which would normally also be expected to write in favour of cutting energy bills. Both, one might think, would also tend to be in favour of things which command huge approval across the Middle England.

As the New Economics Foundation showed shortly afterwards, the regulations update was forecast to cut more than £1bn from the nation's collective energy bill over the next 15 years (it is a progressive saving, obviously, because it only has an impact when you buy a new cooker).[392] And as for the public – as the Women's Institute said after an opinion survey showed 87 per cent of Britons in favour: 'Nobody likes to waste energy, and in fact the survey shows that people want regulations that cut down on waste.'[393]

In this case, the fury about an EU assault on our energy waste failed – the EcoDesign update happened. But it has not always been so.

In late 2016, following years of discussions with

member states, the European Commission was preparing to unveil its latest package of measures and targets on energy, which would run to 2030.[394] Among them was a draft target of improving energy efficiency by 27 per cent. Various bits of analysis showed this to be remarkably unambitious. A 40 per cent improvement appeared achievable.

The target was eventually increased to 30 per cent. But not due to lobbying from Britain. The British government would not support anything more than 27 per cent – one of the reasons, insiders reported, being fear of critical headlines about 'EU diktats'.

Now, all of this happened in the period around the UK's referendum on EU membership, so it is not surprising to see some papers claiming that anything the EU did was damaging and unpopular. But opinions in newspapers are often influenced by think-tanks and lobby groups; and among organisations regularly claiming that energy efficiency policies do not work, we find GWPF.[395,396,397,398]

Had the UK's delegates been more ambitious in the EU negotiations, would we have ended up with a stronger target? Maybe: Britain has historically been an influential voice in the bloc's climate and energy discussions. As a quick *aide-memoire*, the multiple benefits of effective energy efficiency policy are cutting bills, keeping people warm in winter, reducing reliance on imports of gas and coal, and cutting carbon emissions.

The second and much wider-ranging example concerns the batteries of media assaults on energy policy that the contrarian elite launches at key moments. One good example was Energy and Climate Change Secretary Amber Rudd's 'energy reset speech' in November 2015.[399] Over the weekend immediately preceding it, Peter Hitchens in the *Mail on Sunday*[400], Charles Moore in the *Telegraph*[401] and Matt Ridley in *The Times*[402] all contributed columns making remarkably similar points – energy bills were going up because of green policies, the lights were in danger of going out, and anyway all this greenery meant nothing in climate change terms because China and India were continuing to build coal-fired power stations. Moore's final paragraph is one of the finest examples of splenetic indignation in this field that I have come across:

> 'Like most people – possibly everyone – who takes part in the global-warming debate, I do not know what will happen to the temperature of the Earth in a century's time. What I do know, because it is plainly visible, is that the attempt to run the world as if we can control our eco-fate 100 years hence is statistically fantastical, politically impossible, economically ruinous and morally bogus. "The lights are going out all over Europe," lamented Sir Edward Grey in 1914. That was because of a war. Now we are doing our best to put them out all over again, in the name of the common good.'

Wonderful stuff.

And the scare-mongering has been effective. When Ms Rudd delivered her long-awaited speech, the top line was that energy security would now become the most important objective of energy policy.[403] Keeping bills down and reducing carbon emissions – the other two ingredients of the so-called 'energy trilemma' – would still be important, but not quite as important as keeping the lights on.

Something had certainly changed since steers about the speech emerged in the press a few weeks beforehand. Then, it was reported that cost would be the most important leg of the trilemma. From insiders, the story is that what lay behind the change to prioritising energy security was Prime Minister David Cameron's belief, stoked by a slew of cataclysmic newspaper headlines, that the lights were in real danger of going out during the winter.

That was not all. In the period around the speech, journalists were privately briefed that the government thought renewables too expensive and would re-examine their 'hidden costs' – a 'senior energy source' hinting darkly that 'it may well turn out that certain kinds of renewable energy are not quite as cheap as we thought when the billions paid over the years required to support it are taken into account.'[404,405]

There was a claim that Britain needed to build 25 new large power stations to stop the lights going out.[406] There were hints that the government wanted to re-examine the overall pace of decarbonisation mapped out by the already-agreed carbon budgets.

If you are an investor, a banker, an advisor or indeed the boss of a company that builds energy infrastructure, all of this adds up to a single word: 'risk'. If the policy landscape appears volatile, investments look more risky and the cost of financing them goes up. Higher costs will be passed on to the public through energy bills.

In March 2016, the Energy and Climate Change Select Committee concluded its inquiry into investor confidence in the sector thus: 'Investor confidence has been dented by a series of sudden policy changes since the election, which may lead to a hiatus in project developments and threaten the UK's ability to meet its energy security and climate change objectives.'[407] So – not only more expensive energy, but less security and more pollution too.

More pithy was the evidence the Committee took from developers and investors. Andrew Lee, boss of Velocita Energy Developments whose portfolio included wind energy projects in several European countries, told MPs that unstable energy policy made it more expensive to raise finance in Britain than in France: 'In the UK we probably have to add 2 or 3 per cent on to that, because we have learnt from experience that, over the years, [the return] will be salami-sliced back.'[408] Chris Hulatt, co-founder of Octopus Investments, told MPs that the increased risk to investments driven by constant policy tinkering would increase energy costs for Britons by up to £3.14 bn per year – equivalent to about £120 on the average bill.

Remember, as you re-read the passage above, who contends the loudest that Britain's energy policy is 'broken' and makes the shrillest calls for revising energy policy on the basis that it is too – er – expensive.

One could perhaps add to the bill the £180 million that Britons spent on policies designed to provide electricity generation back-up across three winters, which was never needed.[409] Was that outlay partially down to the 500-odd articles scaremongering about risks of 'the lights going out'?

You could argue also that the case for building the Hinkley C nuclear power station, complete with its financing package that will see British billpayers contribute about £1bn to the French government each year, was greatly strengthened by contrarian excoriations on renewables.[410] Indeed, back in 2009, Christopher Booker purred approvingly about Energy Minister John Hutton's declaration that Britain needed new nuclear plants: [411]

> 'Hutton had finally taken on board that unless very dramatic steps were taken to close Britain's approaching energy gap, within a few years she would face a massive crisis. Building windmills was not going to have any effect. The only way to close the gap would be to build new nuclear and coal-fired power stations as fast as it could be done.'

No 'very dramatic steps' were taken; 'windmills' now provide 15 per cent of UK electricity, and the lights have stayed on. Just a bit more expensively than they might have done – thanks, in part, to Britain's energy and climate contrarians.

6
Broadcasting values

As the nationally-owned broadcaster, the BBC is obliged to be impartial. On climate change, that has not always been easy. The months after the Copenhagen summit presented a particular challenge when, as I outlined earlier, there were really two different stories going on: mainstream science continued to outline risks ahead and mainstream politicians continued to say they took it seriously, while in a parallel narrative, the foundations of the edifice were being questioned like never before. But it was not a unique time.

The main problem the BBC faces is this. The science presents a generally consistent overall story. There are many genuine debates between scientists on specific questions, but almost no disagreement over the basic picture: climate change is happening, it is almost certainly driven by emissions of greenhouse gases, the best strategy for dealing with it is to cut emissions as quickly as possible leavened with some adaptation, and doing so will not be economically ruinous.

Yet we have a group of politicians and prominent commentators maintaining that the science is broken and the solutions unaffordable, unworkable and unpopular. At times, those politicians have had traction, such as when Chris Heaton-Harris MP gathered more than 100 MPs' signatures on a letter to the Prime Minister calling for a suspension of onshore wind energy.[412] Those stories must be covered – the BBC would be failing in its duty were it not to cover them. If there is significant backing in Parliament, business or society for a particular policy shift, that ought to be covered too. Yet it should be done in such a way that the evidence from science, economics and public opinion is reflected accurately, ensuring that the public is not misled by interviewees.

And the BBC matters. It is far and away Britons' most-used source of information in the media on energy and climate change. Its position in the media landscape means that it is uniquely prone to political pressure and challenge on its editorial 'position'. And despite the regular attacks it receives from various constituencies, just about everyone also wants it to cover 'their side of the story' because of the credibility BBC coverage brings.

For broadcast and print media alike, subjects involving copious amounts of scientific evidence face an immediate problem: very few people in senior editorial posts have much contact with science. The most important journalistic 'beat', with which editors and presenters have to be familiar, is politics. And in politics, facts are not the most valuable commodity; opinions are far more important. A private tip from a cabinet minister can be more influential, make a more important news story, than any mound of evidence. As one example, evidence that plastic waste poses a major and rapidly increasing threat to ocean life has been around for at least a decade. But what made the UK government take action on it – and what therefore made it a major news story – was Michael Gove's opinion as Environment Secretary that it mattered enough for him to do something about it.

In politics, everyone has a line, everyone is trying to sell something – which means that political journalists have to assume there is spin in everything they hear. By contrast, while opinions are important in science, they are trumped by evidence. A scientist forecasting ice-free summers in the Arctic by mid-century is not spinning a line but extrapolating from a graph made up of hard data points – and if the journalist suspects that the scientist is spinning a line, they can probe into the data itself.

It is a very, very different world from Westminster; and it is not obvious to me that an editor or presenter brought up in a political milieu would automatically internalise this. At least with the written press there is time to check facts if the journalist needs to, but in the context of live radio or television it is not so.

Despite these issues, overall, the BBC does an excellent job of covering climate change. All journalists, myself most certainly included, make mistakes and have off days; but I defy any serious critic to identify systemic flaws in the BBC's climate change coverage.

I will come back to 'those' Today Programme interviews with Nigel Lawson in the next chapter. For now, I want to highlight two ways in the BBC has, I believe, let itself be drawn a little too far into the contrarians' camp.

The first concerns coverage of energy rather than climate change. I hope that I have shown that from the contrarian point of view, the two are inextricably linked: if you accept that climate science indicates a rationale for decarbonisation, then the additional cost of nuclear reactors or renewable energy (when it carried a significant additional cost) is an expense that you will be much more willing to pay than if you plough a 'lukewarmist' or denier furrow. And whereas the BBC has generally done a good job on reporting climate change, its energy coverage – which is usually led by the Business Unit – has not always been forward-looking and evidence-based.

This is perplexing. In most other first-tier news organisations, business teams realised years ago that there is a global energy transition under way, driven largely by companies and investors, and that it presents both opportunities and threats in areas such as jobs, revenue for national exchequers, shares that underpin pension funds, and regional development. All of which generates wonderful opportunities for imaginative and inquisitive journalism. The scientific rationale for decarbonising is an integral part of the story – but often, for businesses and therefore business journalists, not the leading aspect.

The examplars in cottoning on to the energy transition early are the *Financial Times* and *The Economist*, both of which have run coverage on issues such as stranded assets for years. Reuters, spurred perhaps by the rise of Bloomberg as a rival news agency, has also completely 'got' the energy transition story. Outside these institutions, individual journalists such as the *Telegraph*'s Ambrose Evans-Pritchard were 'early adopters'.

By contrast, the BBC's energy coverage sometimes seems stuck in a timewarp. Until recently it was fairly common to hear BBC journalists talking about a 'shortage of generation' – that non-existent 'Blackout

Britain' meme again – or that energy bills were rising because of 'green taxes'. It seems locked in a world in which coal, oil and gas are inherently trusted and reliable – renewables are risky, pricey and unpopular. A world in which energy bills are perpetually rising, and where Britons worry more about their bills than anything else in the climate and energy space.

A recent nadir was its coverage of the cost of energy review which the government commissioned in 2017 from Professor Dieter Helm.[413] As a complaint by the community energy campaign group 10:10 showed, BBC coverage included a welter of mistakes. The television news report completely ignored decarbonisation as one of the government's reasons for commissioning the review, the website story said that 20 per cent of the average energy bill goes to pay for renewables, and the radio news bulletin said that energy bills had doubled in a decade – all of which are incorrect.

Nine months after broadcast, the BBC acknowledged to 10:10 that the last-named was a serious error and issued an apology; bills, as anyone who looks hard enough will find, have actually been falling.[414] However, the website story still carries as fact the erroneous claim that 'green energy taxes, brought in to pay for renewable forms of generation... made up about 20 per cent of household bills' unchallenged.[415] The real figure is 8 per cent; and this is spent on measures that fund energy efficiency improvements as well as renewables.[416]

How BBC Business journalists came to make these elementary errors is unclear to me. But based purely on instinct and experience, I think it is partially that they gave too much credence to the review itself without stopping to probe any of its figures; partially that they did not know some of the basic facts and did not stop to look them up; partially that they have not grasped the importance of decarbonisation for the energy system and indeed for the general public; and partially because constant repetition of memes such as 'costly green taxes' have permeated so far into the fabric that they become the starting assumptions for energy stories.

What appears to be the BBC Business worldview on energy is not unique to them. Five years ago, it also dominated the written press. It is a worldview that is shaped by big, profitable incumbent businesses such as the 'Big Six' energy utilities, with regular assistance from Right-leaning 'think-tanks', several of which are located close to GWPF in Tufton Street. As I noted in Chapter 2, these constituencies helped seed literally hundreds of articles warning that the lights were going to go out; and, amplified at times by friends in Westminster, they were rather successful in propagating the myth until reality intervened.

They have also relentlessly promoted the view that renewables are inherently expensive and unreliable, and that the energy transition is raising energy bills. It is not hard to see the interest that some players have in promoting such stories. But if journalism is doing its job with a proper degree of scepticism, these claims very obviously merit scrutiny.

But the worldview has also been created by editors themselves. Three journalists who frequently cover energy – one for broadcast, two for newspapers – have told me down the years that their editors were really only interested in two stories: whether the lights are going to go out and whether bills are going to rise.

Partly this is just the natural fact that a story highlighting a problem has more traction than one indicating that Armageddon is postponed. But there is also an obvious circularity here in that if these are the stories you publish, they are the ones you come to expect, and so are the ones you are most likely to publish... and so on. Nevertheless, most of UK energy journalism has broken out of this ultra-reductionist worldview – and if they can, the BBC can too.

How the BBC wishes its energy coverage to be is for its bosses to decide. In my view, the organisation is missing a big trick by not getting up to speed on the global energy transition, which – when you step back from the dayglo stories of court cases and elections and Trumpian idiocies and Russian malfeasance – has to be one of the defining stories of our age.

It involves nothing less than the complete re-shaping of the energy system that drove the Industrial Revolution and created the wealth of our modern world – and the Paris Agreement and this year's IPCC special report on the 1.5°C global warming target indicate that it should happen in little more than a single human generation. It will re-shape the geopolitical world order, decentralise and democratise a commodity that has until now been for corporations only, and create new industries while taking others out of commission. It creates a need for a shake-up of pension funds and government revenue streams. Its progress will largely determine whether the human race enters a future of unpredictable and escalating climate impacts, or just significant ones.

Why is that a story you would not want to own?

The second way in which the BBC sometimes trips

itself up is by paying too much attention to the opinion pages of newspapers.

Producers and presenters routinely read the opinion pages, for a number of reasons. Some commentators have genuine insights to shed. Others may proffer interesting tidbits that can be used in interviews. Sometimes they just make a good read. And producers, for radio in particular, are always looking for guests – columnists often make engaging ones, particularly when arguing with each other.

There are, though, two pitfalls into which you can fall through over-regarding newspaper columnists. One is to assume that they all know what they are talking about; the other is to think that in some way they speak for the public mood. In the area of energy and climate change, neither is automatically true.

On climate change, British newspapers' opinion pages have for a decade been dominated by contrarian commentary. Matt Ridley, James Delingpole, Christopher Booker, Melanie Phillips, Dominic Lawson, Bjorn Lomborg, Charles Moore, are pitted against – who, exactly? Among regular writers on the issue, really only *The Guardian*'s George Monbiot.

Despite the regular complaint of contrarians that they are the small guys who cannot get a hearing, it is quite clear where the balance has lain – and quite clear what message BBC producers and editors will have received if they fell into the two cardinal traps of assuming that commentators universally know of what they write and/or reflect public opinion. Did the relentless stream of opinion articles downplaying climate change and claiming that clean energy was unaffordable, unreliable and unpopular – even when the evidence pointed in the other direction – subconsciously sway editorial decision-making and lines of interviewing?

What one might call the 'Nick Robinson defence', after the Today Programme presenter made it in a *New Statesman* article following criticism of the second totemic Today Programme interview with Nigel Lawson in 2017, is that 'these people deserve to be heard on the BBC'.[417]

In principle – to adopt a phrase once used in politics with a different meaning – I agree with Nick. One should never shy away from a battle of ideas. But the Robinson defence is contestable in at least three ways.

First comes the very obvious point that airtime is precious; just because you *can* run a certain item with a certain contibutor in a certain programme does not mean it is the best choice to make. On subjects such as energy and climate change, there are many worthwhile and very genuine debates to be had that go way beyond the traditional 'is it/isn't it?' formulation. Right now we could be listening to informed debates on issues such as whether climate change will bring colder winters to the UK, and if so, how; to what extent Russia's teetering economic reliance on oil and gas exports is behind its current political manoeuvrings; or whether half of the cars on the road in a decade's time will really be self-driving electric ones. If the BBC really went out on a limb we could even be listening to an investigation into how it came to be that only 5 per cent of the British public knew that the British public backed renewable energy, including tough interviews with people who have regularly and loudly claimed the opposite. Would this not be a more enlightening use of precious airtime?

The second challenge is about representation. There is a temptation to view organisations such as GWPF as the counterparts to Greenpeace and the rest of the environmental movement; and in terms of what they each campaign for, there is a degree of diametric opposition. But in terms of societal legitimacy, there is no comparison. The RSPB has 1.2 million members. Friends of the Earth UK has 300,000 supporters. WWF-UK has 600,000 supporters including 120,000 members. These groups receive the majority of their funding from the public, through membership and donations. GWPF by contrast is estimated to have at most a few hundred paying supporters; the three so far publicly identified are all wealthy individuals with a background in finance.[418] If campaigning against action on climate change were popular, you might imagine that the good burghers of Britain would be beating a path to GWPF's door with donations and good wishes. They are manifestly not. So yes, Nick – do air those views, but please, before you do so, have a read of this book's final chapter and make sure you are clear just how few people hold them.

The third challenge to the Robinson defence is also around representation. For a public service broadcaster, should not the opinion of each ordinary licence-fee payer, perhaps each citizen, be equally important? There is a very obvious danger in allowing representation to centre on people who move in the same social circles as presenters and editors – which often will mean newspaper columnists, a group which on climate change, as we have seen, is collectively skewed towards the contrarian end of the spectrum.

The over-easy reliance on columnists was

highlighted rather exquisitely in an exchange on the Today Programme in February 2018, in which we learned that Quentin Letts, the *Daily Mail* diarist and *Spectator* regular, had switched the radio station to which he listens in the mornings. Letts explained that he had become fed up with the Today Programme's diet of Westminster politics and hard news. Presenter Justin Webb interjected that the programme's new editor, Sarah Sands, wanted to move away from such material, which was exactly why the Today Programme was covering a 'soft' issue such as the nation's changing listening habits. To which Letts responded 'I know Sarah Sands...'

Well – indeed; which is exactly why his change of listening habits, rather than those of any other licence-fee payer, was selected to grace the nation's airwaves.

The BBC surely has to do better than this. Newspaper commentators have columns for a range of reasons, which includes being insightful but also includes reflecting the editor's or proprietor's world view. If the BBC pays undue account to columnists, it is also giving undue prominence to their editors' and proprietors' worldviews above all others. When individuals' listening habits are the issue, this is ephemera; but on climate change, the dangers should be only too obvious.

From time to time – progressively less frequently, I perceive – BBC presenters still make extraordinary gaffes on very basic points. Thus for example Nick Robinson's statement during an interview in July 2018, at the height of the heatwave, that in although 'it is tempting to link the heat we've seen and the drought as well to global warming...there is no clear evidential link to the weather over a few weeks, is there?' This came just four days after virtually every major news outlet, including the BBC website, reported on a scientific study indicating that human-induced climate change made the heatwave at least twice as likely to occur.[419] It came 14 years after the first scientific study showing fingerprints of climate change on an extreme weather event.[420] Thus, also, his fellow Today presenter John Humphreys' repeated reference to '1.5 percent' of global warming rather than 1.5 degrees when covering the IPCC's special report in October.[421] By now, it really should be possible to get such things right.

Despite these gripes, I return to the point I made a few pages earlier: overall, the BBC's track record on reporting climate change, both in news and non-news programmes, is of a really high standard, especially given the political pressures at play. Scientists and others who complain about its occasional failings have every right to do so – but at the same time, they should appreciate what they have. Britain, and the British media, would be a poorer place without a robust BBC.

Fortunately for the British public, things are changing at the level of discourse almost as quickly as in science itself. As I will show in the next chapter, the hiatus in balanced commentary and evidence-based policymaking is very nearly over.

7
Reality begins to bite

In early 2017, little more than a year after the Paris climate summit and a couple of months into the era of President Trump, the *Daily Telegraph's* assistant editor Jeremy Warner penned a highly symbolic column.[422]

The headline brilliantly summed up the article's thesis: 'Bad news petrol-heads; Trump or no Trump, the green revolution is coming to get you'. Paris deal or no Paris deal, Warner argued, the future now lies in clean, smart, decentralised and democratised energy. The Donald, he said, would not be able to put the clean genie back in the bottle – nor would doing so be in American interests.

> 'It is the economics which will in future drive the transition to a low emissions environment, not government intervention and carbon taxes.
>
> 'Never mind electric cars and LED light bulbs, peering into the future, we can already see a world of virtually cost free energy, of smart phones powered by radiant light alone, and of office blocks and houses that derive all their energy from the sun, the wind, and their own waste. In terms of cost, longevity, and efficiency, all these technologies are showing almost exponential rates of improvement...

> 'Is the new administration seriously proposing to give up the country's world leading position in clean energy for the essentially already obsolete technology of the internal combustion engine and the coal fired power plant? Of course not.'

Jeremy Warner is no green ideologue. He cannot be; he is writing business commentary for a business audience. Neither the Paris Agreement nor all the climate science in the world is as important here as the movement of capital. And once capital begins moving to clean energy, clean energy costs fall, more capital moves in that direction, costs fall again... and so on.

Allied to innovation, this rather than international agreements is the power re-shaping the energy world most profoundly, in Warner's judgement; and he is largely right. One of the issues that contrarians apparently find hard to understand about agreements such as that concluded in Paris is that governments adopt them largely because they tally with national development plans – reinforcing, but not dictating, the direction of travel.

The article tacitly acknowledged a significant change in economic reality. Until recently, the theoretical and real worlds of energy and climate change economics had been at loggerheads. Climate change agreements, economic analyses including the Stern Review, indeed the science itself, indicated that a shift away from investment in fossil fuels towards clean technologies was the logical pathway – a little more expense now averting a vastly more costly set of impacts in future. But in the real world, investors continued to pile into oil and gas as though the future were an iteration of the past. As Warner noted, within a very short space of time this equation had changed markedly; and it has carried on changing. Now, not only is onshore wind energy the cheapest form of new electricity generation in the UK (were the government to facilitate a route to market)[423] – renewables, led by solar, are the cheapest option in at least 60 countries, a number that is expanding every year.[424,425]

Investment is following. In 2016, two-thirds of the new generating capacity added around the world consisted of wind and solar power.[426] That figure comes from the International Energy Agency (IEA), not a green lobby group. The IEA forecasts a 43 per cent increase in global renewable energy capacity in just five years. In India – very much a bellwether in the energy field because of its huge population and need to develop – 90 per cent of new generating capacity will come from wind and solar. The IEA has historically been a conservative body on renewable energy, so one can be fairly sure that these forecasts will turn out to be underestimates.

Price trends are not the only factor in capital's flight to clean energy. As the *Wall Street Journal* observed earlier this year:

> 'Renewable-energy plants also face fewer challenges than traditional power plants. Nuclear-power plants have been troubled by mostly technical delays, while plants burning fossil fuels face regulatory uncertainties due to concerns about climate change. And pension funds, seeking long-term stable returns, have invested heavily in wind farms and solar parks, allowing developers to get cheaper

financing.'[427]

A quick look at China and India will illustrate the point. A decade ago, it was said – and it was true – that China was building one coal-fired power station a week. Now it is building an equivalent amount of clean energy capacity every week, and plans to continue doing that until 2030 at least.[428]

Coal-fired power stations are still being built as well – but they are really the legacy of investment decisions made four or five years ago. And the rate of build is slowing. Globally, the number of coal-fired power stations starting construction in 2017 was a quarter of that two years previously.[429] China and India illustrate the trend most starkly. In 2015, 66GW of new coal-fired power station capacity opened in China.[430] In 2016, the figure was 47; and in 2017, 37. The equivalent figures for India are 21, 19 and 9.[431]

This is not surprising given that new power stations are operating less and less of the time as they are out-competed by cheaper renewables, hence the economics are getting progressively more difficult. A new coal-fired power station in China will now be in operation for less than half of the time; essentially, the country has far more than it needs.[432]

In India, the utilisation rate is also down. The government's draft National Electricity Plan calculates that it does not need to build any more coal-fired power stations in the next five years.[433] Those under construction can finish: after that, a moratorium on new build is eminently possible. The Central Electricity Authority says that in the early 2020s, it expects coal-fired power stations to be needed on average for only

48 per cent of the time, with some in use hardly at all. The industry body the Association of Power Producers says that plant needs to be running at least 65 per cent of the time to be economically viable.[434] The implication is obvious.

In the United States, Donald Trump has vowed to re-build the coal industry. This should of course be anathema to any free-market commentator, involving as it would a vast amount of state intervention to distort the market in favour of coal; because the market is taking the US in one direction only. Thirty-nine gigawatts (GW) of coal-fired generating capacity have closed over the three years 2015-17, and the number forecast to close this year, 13GW, indicates that advent of Trump is not reducing the rate at all.[435] More than three-quarters of the coal-fired power stations in Europe and North America are over 30 years old; and with the average retirement age being 37, in these two continents coal-fired generation is not an industry with anything of the spring chicken about it.[436]

So pronounced is the global flight from coal that on current trends the capacity of coal-fired plant being retired around the world is set to exceed the amount opening by 2022.[437]

Even if President Trump were not pushing against the direction of the market, there would still be an inherent tension in his plans to expand US coal and gas production simultaneously. Both commodities sell into international as well as domestic markets: expanding shale gas production further will push down the international price, which of course makes it harder for coal to compete.

A switch from coal and gas to renewables in the

power sector is not by itself an economy-wide clean energy transition sufficient to deliver the Paris Agreement targets. But it is an essential part of one. Fundamentally, the transition – as described by the IPCC and many others – looks like this:

1) Make all energy use as efficient as possible
2) Switch all power generation to low-carbon forms – renewables, nuclear, low-carbon gas (such as biogas), or fossil gas with carbon capture and storage (CCS)
3) Use expanded electricity production and/or other low-carbon technologies (such as hydrogen) to power those parts of the economy where fossil fuels are currently burned directly – most notably, oil in transport, coal and gas in heating
4) Implement bespoke solutions in those sectors where the three-part prescription above does not apply, such as agriculture.

All elements of that transition are in progress. They have reached varying stages and are happening at a range of speeds; whether everything will occur quickly enough to meet the Paris Agreement targets is currently a matter of conjecture. The IPCC's Special Report on the 1.5°C Paris target indicates a need to halve emissions globally by 2030 and reach net zero around mid-century.[438] So it is not a trifling matter. But there is no doubt that some parts of the clean energy transition, let by energy efficiency improvements and renewables but with electric vehicles fast catching up, are very much now rooted in the real economy.

This should be a matter for celebration. Thousands

of coal miners die each year, mainly in developing countries – possibly as many as 12,000 a year.[439] In addition to climate-warming carbon dioxide, burning coal puts oxides of sulphur and nitrogen into the air, together with particulates and traces of heavy metals such as mercury. It therefore raises rates of lung and heart disease and some cancers.[440] The World Health Organisation estimates that 3.7 million people die prematurely each year from outdoor air pollution.[441] Coal is not the only source, but it is a significant one. Switching away from coal to carbon-free sources of electricity, and running cars on electricity or hydrogen rather than oil, will make society healthier, especially the poor who, we know, are more exposed to air pollution, even in the UK.

A clean energy transition has other advantages too. Renewables generate much more employment than fossil-fuel technologies; in the US, more than 200,000 people work in the solar industry[442], four times the number in coal.[443] Insulated homes are warm homes, reducing fuel poverty and improving people's health. Reducing the need to extract and transport oil will cut the number of environmentally damaging spills and leaks (although not all low-carbon energy technologies are entirely free of health and environmental impacts).

Not all aspects of the clean energy transition are being enacted as sensibly as they could be in all countries. The UK has made its share of sub-optimal decisions, from adopting the Green Deal energy efficiency policy to making its first new nuclear power station in a generation about as expensive as it could have done. But as a general point, the social and environmental desirability of the low-carbon transition is really beyond dispute.

Judging by opinion surveys, the vast majority of the public sees the benefits – not least as the method of keeping climate change within 'safe' limits. Indeed, if contrarians have been trying to sway public opinion, their ineffectiveness is quite remarkable. After a decade of being told that wind turbines are ugly, unreliable, absurdly expensive and unpopular, more than three-quarters of the public supports them. In survey after survey, only 2 per cent 'strongly opposes' onshore wind power.[444] Likewise more than two-thirds of the population supports the UK's Climate Change Act, which we have been relentlessly informed will cripple our economy; just one-tenth opposes it.[445] The Paris Agreement commands similar support.

The public has been repeatedly told that they do not like subsidies within the energy system – and yet they stubbornly refuse to believe what they are told they believe, with 85 per cent backing subsidies that pay for renewable energy and for measures that cut energy waste.[446] Only 3 per cent put gas-fired power stations top of their list of desirable electricity generation technologies; the figure for renewables is 42 per cent. Columnist after columnist tells the public how crucial it is that we 'get fracking', yet the public does not seem to be listening, with opposition outweighing support by nearly two to one.[447] Despite massive publicity over Britain's 'crippling high' energy bills, more than twice as many people (75% to 30%) are concerned about climate change than about their energy bill.[448]

If the contrarian movement has failed to change the course of either the real economy or public opinion, its failure at political level is even starker. All 195 IPCC member states endorsed the Fifth Assessment Report in 2013/14. That means they all accept that evidence of climate change is beyond dispute, that almost certainly humanity's greenhouse gas emissions are the main cause, and that the further climate change progresses, the greater risk it poses of 'severe, pervasive and irreversible impacts'.[449]

They also accept that constraining global warming to 2°C means bringing greenhouse gas emissions down to 'net zero' in the second half of the century – a goal to which those self-same nations expressly re-committed in the Paris Agreement just over a year later.[450] October 2018 saw similarly unanimous acceptance from all countries making up the IPCC for its 1.5°C report, meaning they accept conclusions such as:

- 'Human activities are estimated to have caused approximately 1.0°C of global warming above pre-industrial levels...'
- 'Estimated anthropogenic global warming is currently increasing at 0.2°C per decade...'
- 'Climate-related risks to health, livelihoods, food security, water supply, human security, and economic growth are projected to increase with global warming of 1.5°C and increase further with 2°C'
- Achieving the 1.5°C target means halving carbon emissions by 2030 and bringing them to net zero around mid-century – and although tough, this is feasible.

That is 'all countries' – including the US, China and

India, and Gulf states such as Saudi Arabia whose exchequers depend heavily on fossil fuels.

If you have spent the last few years campaigning against such an outcome, this is quite some failure. Yes, Donald Trump may have declared that the US will leave the Paris Agreement – but it has not left, and may never do so.[451] And although Trumpism may slow the clean energy transition taking place in the US, it will not change the fundamental direction of travel. China and India, the most important nations when it comes to both the emissions and the energy technology of the immediate future, are both firmly inside the Agreement. Brazil, too, is staying in, following a change of heart by President-elect Bolsonaro.[452]

In the wake of the Paris Agreement, the world's giant energy companies are beginning to invest more time and money in a low-carbon transition. Since the Paris summit, both Shell and BP have for the first time published 'scenarios' showing how the energy system can evolve in order to keep global warming well below 2°C.[453,454] Total says it is planning for the future with the IEA's 2°C scenario 'as a baseline' and has set targets for diversifying away from oil and gas.[455] Even ExxonMobil has analysed 2°C scenarios and worked out what they would mean for the company's business model.[456]

This does not mean that these companies believe global warming will be kept below 2°C, still less that they will lobby for that outcome; but for the first time, they are acknowledging it as a possibility.

Concern about climate change, from governments, shareholders and customers, is one factor that has brought them to this position. But far more important is the mix of threats to the companies' market value looming on the horizon: divestment, legal action, and above all a rapid low-carbon transition that slashes the value of their assets. Fossil fuel companies, along with governments and US states, are facing some of the 1000+ legal cases currently underway around the world on climate change, a situation that poses reputational risks as well as financial ones.[457]

In Gulf states that have the oil and gas industry as an integral arm of government, leaders are also beginning to regard moving to a low-carbon economy as feasible and desirable. Saudi Arabia's national development plan, Saudi Vision 2030, has diversification of the economy as a central objective, and plans for both renewable and nuclear energy are in place.[458] Again, a prime mover is the possibility of abrupt declines in the value of company assets – which here means the nation's assets. One suspects that science indicating that Middle East cities could see daytime temperatures soar above 70°C in coming decades has also concentrated minds – as has some of the cheapest solar power anywhere in the world.[459]

Of course, Saudi Arabia will continue to extract and sell oil and gas. In fact, its national plan is indicative of a mindset that appears to be developing in a number of oil exporting countries including Mexico and Norway: we should develop renewable energy for use at home, given its rapidly falling cost, while extracting as much of our oil and gas as possible for export. Which is fine in theory, but in practice is likely to end in failure; because countries without oil have even more of an incentive to adopt low-carbon energy and transport technologies, raising the question of who exactly will be importing.

Car companies meanwhile are mixed on the move to electrically-powered motoring. A number, including Volvo, BMW and the Nissan-Renault-Mitsubishi alliance, clearly believe the near-future to be electric. Electric cars are significantly cheaper to run than petrol and diesel (much cheaper fuel, far fewer moving parts to service); and in late 2017, MoneySupermarket.com calculated that in the UK, on a lifetime basis, they are already cost-competitive.[460] Nissan believes that on purchase price alone, EVs will be comparable by 2025.[461] In many countries, the availability of charging points is an issue, as is rapid depletion of battery charge on motorways; which is why some manufacturers are holding back, and one, Toyota, pursuing hydrogen-powered cars. Although enthusiasm for low-carbon motoring is mixed across the traditional automotive giants, the mood is certainly a world away from that in evidence a decade ago, when the sector was more or less united in its adherence to petroleum.

There are two other factors that could lead to a much swifter change to electric motoring than is generally assumed. One is China. Brands such as BYD, SAIC, FAW, Geely, BAIC and Dongfeng might not be household names in the West yet (although Geely should be, given that it owns Volvo) – but they soon will be.[462]

The Chinese government has a complex set of policy measures aimed at making it the centre of global EV manufacturing – subsidies for purchase, regulations on manufacturers, incentives that produce higher energy density batteries, and deals that consolidate smaller companies into bigger ones.[463] Sales of EVs and hybrids could pass the one million mark this year; and one of the reasons for building a thriving domestic market is in order to dominate outside China. What this implies for the Western motorist is a likely transition in car brand awareness and ownership similar to that seen in the 60s, 70s and 80s when Japanese, then Korean, then Malaysian manufacturers made huge inroads into Western markets. The potential for a similar slide by the big Western marques if they are off the pace is even greater this time.

The second factor is new entrants. Because the nature of electric vehicles is not yet consolidated, companies such as Google and Dyson can spring into the market with innovative offerings. Deals are possible that combine ownership of or access to an electric vehicle with a contract for household energy. It is a far more open field than in the pure petrol/diesel era. For consumers, the big attraction is the sharp spur that these new entrants apply to the rump end of the incumbents, for whom the choice is to match the innovators or perish.

All of this should logically excite advocates of free markets and international trade – because it should lead to better and cheaper products for us to use.

The same is true in the electricity sector. Battery storage and demand-shifting providers are offering more cost-effective ways to balance the system, saving money for customers and reducing the extent to which the grid needs strengthening. Early experience with the giant Tesla battery in South Australia shows it is preventing gas-fired generators from gaming the market – reducing the chances of prices spiking to absurd levels at times of peak demand.[464]

In the UK, new retailers are taking on the 'Big Six'

and often winning, mainly through providing better customer satisfaction. For generating companies, the smaller scale of renewables makes it easier to enter the field than was the case when giant coal, gas and nuclear power stations were the only option.

So, at least in electricity and transport, a transition to clean technology is a reality. It is not always smooth and well-managed; and in any nation, a change of government can have a major impact on the pace of transformation. But against all the tenets of contrarianism, it is most definitely happening.

In the UK, opposition to the low-carbon transition is largely confined to the politics of the Right; there is some opposition in trade unions with members in the oil and gas, but that has always had limited traction. And on the political Right is where the contrarians have suffered their most recent and most spectacular defeats.

Remember where the battleground was located just four years ago. Owen Paterson MP called for repeal of the Climate Change Act. The media listened – he made his case on the BBC's most influential radio programmes, newspapers carried approving articles, and fellow MPs and Peers endorsed his case. Quite possibly this contributed to Prime Minister David Cameron bringing the curtain down on his pledge to lead the 'greenest ever government', with the Conservative Party's 2015 General Election manifesto promising an end to onshore wind and solar farms and a boost for fracking.

Fast forward to 2018. Currently the discussion is not on repealing the Climate Change Act, but on strengthening it – and the question is not 'whether to' but 'how far to'. And this is being driven by Conservative cabinet ministers, not backbenchers. The most likely outcome will be that the government pledges to eliminate Britain's greenhouse gas emissions, enshrining in law a net zero emissions target with a date around mid-century.

How far things have turned around, and how quickly. And again, if you have made it your business to campaign against such things – what a defeat this must look like.

Newspapers that once dismissed climate change and clean energy have had to change their positions. In 2014, the *Telegraph* went 'all-in' on Owen Paterson's GWPF speech in a way that today looks extraordinary.

Almost inevitably it was kicked off by Christopher Booker who suggested on the Sunday preceding the speech that Paterson would 'save us from an unimaginable energy disaster,' warning that 'the reality of the situation now facing us is even more alarming than anything I have reported on this subject before.'[465]

On Monday, political correspondent Chris Hope previewed the speech, telling us that Paterson would warn: 'In the short and medium term, costs to consumers will rise dramatically, but there can only be one ultimate consequence of this policy: the lights will go out at some time in the future.'[466] Two days later, a leader article warned that if ministers did not take Paterson's prescription seriously, 'then the next government, of whatever stripe, will need to explain to the country why they could have prevented the lights going out, but didn't.'[467] A further two days on, Emily Gosden's news article highlighted Paterson's claim that 'The effects of climate change have been 'consistently and widely exaggerated' in scientific forecasts.'[468]

On the Saturday after the speech, Charles Moore's encomium told us that the UK could not hit its climate change targets, neither could Europe, and anyway this did not matter because China would never curb its carbon emissions.[469] On Sunday, Paterson reprised his speech in a sit-down interview with Liam Halligan, assuring us that: 'The Climate Change Act is completely disastrous – it's been a shock for me in recent months to realise it won't work in practice. You simply can't build all the required non-carbon generation.'[470] There was a further reprise in a leader column the following week, which contended that: 'There is also a case for suspending the provisions of the Climate Change Act, to buy Britain some time to get itself out of this mess.'[471]

If the *Telegraph*'s editors felt Paterson's intervention really merited this much attention – and no scrutiny at all – that is a matter for them. But what a blow the paper delivered to its own credibility. Energy bills have since gone down rather than up. Neither David Cameron nor Theresa May has even come close to needing 'to explain to the country why they could have prevented the lights going out, but didn't.' The articles were followed by three successive 'warmest years', and China's coal use and carbon emissions slowed.

Above all, Paterson's predictions have not turned into reality. Somehow, we have 'kept building the required non-carbon generation' that he warned was impossible, without a mass switch to SMRs. A shale gas industry of substance remains a remote prospect.

As Jeremy Warner's *Telegraph* commentary three years later demonstrates, a newspaper that wants to be relevant cannot continue to ignore real world trends. The cost falls in renewable energy, the car giants' enthusiasm for electric vehicles, the swift rise of flexible technologies such as demand shifting and battery storage, and the steel industry's switch from old-fashioned blast furnaces to electric arc technology have been unmissable. As newspapers from the *Financial Times* onwards have realised, if you want to have credibility with your readers, you need to reflect the world as it is, not as it was or as you would like it to be.

Oil and gas will continue to be massively important sectors for years to come. But already, stranded assets, decommissioning and divestment are standard stories, sitting alongside the traditional fare of annual profits, mergers and exploration. In April 2018, a survey of fund managers in top investment companies such as BlackRock and Schroders found that 89 per cent believe climate change will begin to affect oil companies' valuations within five years; just a year previously, the figure had been 46 per cent.[472] Companies with big stakes in renewables and EVs, from Ørsted to Tesla, are now as much a focus for business journalists as the big oil and gas players.

Even supporters of contrarianism acknowledge reality in their business lives. City financier Neil Record is a director of the Global Warming Policy Forum and a GWPF donor.[473] Despite that, the company that he founded, Record Currency Management, seems convinced of the rationale for a low-carbon transition. Its website tells us that it '...minimises its carbon footprint through the responsible procurement of goods and services and offsetting its remaining carbon emissions by investments in renewable energy projects in emerging markets. Record has been a certified Carbon Neutral Company since 2007.'[474]

8
Shots in the foot prove fatal

The changes in the real world of energy costs and technologies have been glaringly unmissable right across journalism. As has the end of the 'global warming slowdown' story; whatever the details of equilibrium climate sensitivity and ice-sheet hysteresis loops, to have three years in succession breaking the global temperature record is an unmistakable pointer that the world really is heating up.

For Britons and others in Northern Europe, the 2018 heatwave provided an inescapable indicator that 'normal' appears to be changing – and scientists have already shown that climate change made the heatwave at least twice as likely.[475]

The breadth of the social consensus on climate change has also, I think, crept up on editors who were previously doubtful: when you have the Pope, the military, doctors, the Church of England, the National Trust, the RSPB, the National Farmers' Union, the Scouts, the RNLI, the England Cricket Board, the Women's Institute, Sir David Attenborough and even arguably the Queen all lining up behind increasing action on climate change, the contrarian furrow begins to look more than a little friendless. With Conservative MPs now accepting the overwhelming popularity of energy efficiency measures and renewables and acknowledging that they need to say and do more on climate change if they are to win back young voters, the days when Owen Paterson, David Davies and Christopher Chope spoke for the back-benches appear to be over. The contrarian lights are indeed going out in Westminster, just as they are in Fleet Street.

There is a case for arguing that the contrarian community itself is largely responsible for its gradual slide from relevance.

In 2008, as I have outlined, there was a case for looking quizzically at the climate change consensus. And although not all of the quizzing was constructive, any proper reading of these years has to acknowledge that the unvaryingly harsh scrutiny from climate-sceptic circles brought improvements to analysis and discourse. At the BBC, for example, we sharpened up our usage of terms such as 'climate change', 'the greenhouse effect' and 'global warming' in response to scrutiny.

On the other hand, if you proclaim yourself a 'sceptic' – still more if you claim to appeal to reason – then your reputation rests on continuing to be sceptical. If evidence changes, so must opinions and output; otherwise you lose any right to claim words such as 'sceptic' and 'reasonable' as your own.

In February 2014, the BBC Today Programme invited Nigel Lawson to discuss climate change with Sir Brian Hoskins, a veteran climate scientist and at the time chair of the Grantham Centre at Imperial College London.[476] During the interview, Lawson claimed that:

- No global warming had been measured over the 'last 15, 16, 17 years'
- No global increase had been observed in extreme weather events, and the IPCC had said so
- Recently, the Met Office had forecast a dry winter
- Continuing to reduce emissions would 'return us to pre-industrial standards of living'.

All these statements either miss out important caveats or are just wrong. Global warming *was* observed over the period in question – the issues were a) whether the degree of warming was statistically significant, and b) whether or not it had progressed at a markedly lower rate than in the preceding decades.

On extreme weather events, while it is true that there had not been a documented increase in all types of event in all parts of the world, enough changes had been detected for the IPCC to conclude: 'Changes in many extreme weather and climate events have been observed since about 1950'.[477] Among the types of event linked to climate change it listed heatwaves in parts of Europe, Asia and Australia, and heavy rainfall in North America and Europe. So, no global increase – but not nothing, either.

The Met Office had not forecast a dry winter – it had said that the odds of a drier-than-average winter were marginally higher than the odds of a wetter-than-usual winter, which is not a forecast.[478]

As to the claim that reducing emissions would return us to pre-industrial standards of living – it is an opinion, but the basis for it is hard to fathom given that over the previous couple of decades the UK, along with most developed countries, had reduced its greenhouse gas emissions while growing its economy.

Environment groups were up in arms about the decision to invite Lawson on air – still more so that the discussion evolved in such a way that Lawson, who is not a scientist, was able to pass judgement on the science as elucidated by Hoskins, who is. The set-up of the discussion, pitting a professional scientist against a non-scientist with very much a minority view, certainly seemed at odds with the BBC Trust's Review of science coverage.

But there is another way of looking at what became known in some circles as 'LawsonGate': that the person who came out of it losing most was Nigel Lawson himself. In the internet age, no-one can make controversial claims apparently based on publicly-available documents and expect people not to go and look at those documents to check the veracity of those claims. Which, of course, people did – and talked publicly about – and talked publicly about again when the BBC concluded that the interview had not been conducted in line with its editorial standards.[479] Each iteration of the conversation highlighted the gulf between the entirety of the evidence and Lord Lawson's distillation of it.

Despite the peer's subsequent claim that the BBC had 'banned' him from discussing climate change[480] – a claim immediately amplified in a *Spectator* editorial[481] – he was back on the Today Programme to discuss climate change in August 2017. Here, his claims included that:

- The UK has 'among the highest energy costs in the world'

- We do not subsidise fossil fuels
- (Again) there has been no global increase in extreme weather events
- 'Over the last ten years, the global temperature has declined.'

It is obviously sensible to compare Britain's energy costs with countries of similar wealth and geography. And, compared with other European nations, UK energy prices are below average for domestic gas, domestic electricity and industrial gas; only for industrial electricity are they higher than average.

Fossil fuels are subsidised – to the tune of about $500bn per year globally if one uses traditional definitions of 'subsidy', 10 times that amount if you include factors such as the damage they cause through air pollution and climate impacts.[482,483]

While the extreme weather statement was again technically correct, the science of climate attribution had moved on significantly in the three years since the earlier interview, and increasingly scientists are finding that individual extreme events are being made more likely or more intense by climate change. One such is Storm Desmond, which so devasted Cumbria and other parts of the UK in December 2015.[484]

The most obviously wrong statement, though, was that the global temperature had fallen. The exact phrase Lawson used was: '...according – again – to the official figures, during this past ten years, if anything, mean global temperature, average world temperature, has slightly declined.' To anyone who had been following the news even cursorily, this was very out of kilter with a reality in which 2014, 2015 and 2016 had each set a new high for the global average temperature. And indeed, Lawson's own GWPF soon acknowledged the error – in the process revealing that the claim was not based on 'official figures' but on interpretations of them by other climate contrarians.[485]

These two Today Programme outings were dwarfed as shots in one's own foot, though, by the 'What's the Point of the Met Office?' fiasco in August 2015. 'What's the Point of...' is an occasional series on BBC Radio Four presented by *Daily Mail* diarist and *Spectator* regular Quentin Letts, in which Quentin – to quote the BBC's blurb – casts his 'witty but thought-provoking' gaze on icons of British life.[486]

The Met Office is a 'natural' for inclusion. But what the programme's producers clearly failed to realise was that the Met Office has for at least a decade been a key target for contrarian ire. It is surely not a huge leap to conclude that this is because it co-hosts the HadCRUT temperature record. Had the producers known this, they might, one presumes, have stayed their hand.

All BBC output has to fit within a set of editorial guidelines that are designed to guarantee basic values of public service journalism – accuracy, fairness, impartiality, and so on – while allowing inquiry and creativity to flourish.[487] I became rather familiar with the guidelines during my years covering climate change given the number of complaints raised against my reporting (none upheld, in case you are wondering); rather more familiar, it seemed on listening to 'What's the Point of the Met Office?', than the programme's producers.

As I wrote in *The Guardian* at the time, it 'not so much ignored the editorial guidelines as burned them to cinders in a joyous coal-fired conflagration'.[488]

Balance went missing: interviewees included Graham Stringer (Labour) and Peter Lilley (Conservative) – but producers had clearly not clocked that both were advisors to Nigel Lawson's GWPF.[489] Letts began by describing the Met Office's position on climate change as 'not uncontroversial', whereas in reality – as I noted in *The Guardian* article – it is 'so uncontroversial as to be shared by every major national science academy and well over 90 per cent of climate scientists'. False claims included the (by now familiar) one that the Met Office had forecast a dry winter for 2013/14.

Astoundingly, Letts ended the programme by claiming that while the Met Office was good at short-term weather forecasting, its record on climate science was not so hot – and that it had indulged in 'political lobbying'.

On iPlayer, you can now listen back to Quentin Letts asking what is the point of the National Trust, the Army Reserve, the Methodists, the London black cab, the British Board of Film Classification and golf. You cannot, though, listen to him taking apart the Met Office. So bad was the programme that, as well as issuing an unusually rapid and fulsome apology, the BBC pulled the programme from its on-demand service – an extraordinary measure.[490]

In large part, the programme appears to have emerged as it did due to a combination of the strand falling under the Religion and Ethics Department, which is not used to covering the science and politics of climate change, and an unusually heavy workload for the producers involved. Nevertheless, its cast list and its editorial direction did not come about by accident; an individual, or perhaps an organisation, must have seen the opportunity in the BBC's schedules so soon before the UN climate summit in Paris, and constructed a plan to steer the programme in this particular direction.

The bigger question, though, is this: who, and what cause, was ultimately damaged by What's the Point of the Met Office?

It is surely the contrarians.

Within the BBC, both the Lawson interviews and What's the Point Of...? led to more discussion about covering climate change properly, and more training for non-science staff. It is certain that future attempts to crowbar contrarian arguments onto the airwaves will receive more scrutiny.

The logical culmination materialised this September, when the BBC announced a new online learning module for producers, presenters and reporters on climate change.[491] As I wrote at the time in *The Guardian*, the main message this sends externally is that the BBC has stopped caring about the occasional bleat over 'bias' and 'censorship' from columnists such as Chris Booker or James Delingpole, because – why should it care?[492] As I concluded: 'If BBC bosses have decided that from now on they are going to free output from the occasional grip of the UK's climate contrarian elite and stand up for evidence – good on them.'

More importantly, these episodes exposed the lack of real evidence now available in the contrarian stable. If there were serious objections to the consensus picture of climate change, here were golden opportunities to raise them. Instead, Nigel Lawson, Peter Lilley, Graham Stringer and Quentin Letts showed that their quivers are now virtually empty of anything that looks like real evidence. As I wrote when the BBC issued its apology on 'What's the Point of...?': 'Rooted in rhetorical power rather than factual rigour, grossly error-strewn, demonstrably one-eyed... what's the point of presenting your case at all, if that's the case you present?'[493]

In newspapers, the credibility given to the contrarian world view is also diminishing. Following criticism of 'What's the Point of the Met Office?', the *Daily Mail* gave Christopher Booker a column to defend its diarist's programme and amplify a number of the arguments. After a formal complaint from me to the *Mail* on accuracy grounds, it had to make five corrections to Booker's article.[494] In my experience, the *Mail* takes complaints seriously, and this will presumably not have helped Booker's internal cause.

At its stablemate, the *Mail on Sunday*, David Rose achieved the rare distinction of having three complaints about his articles upheld by the industry regulator, the Independent Press Standards Organisation (IPSO), within a single year.[495] Only one of them was on climate change – the other two concerned UK policing and court cases.[496,497]

The climate change article, in February 2017, claimed that the global temperature record maintained by the US National Oceanic and Atmospheric Administration (NOAA) had been manipulated to create the impression that the world was heating up more than it really was – specifically, that there had been no pause in global warming.[498] It went on to claim that this amended record, formally published in a scientific paper in June 2015,[499] had been pivotal in persuading world leaders to adopt the Paris Agreement.

Following a complaint by Bob Ward of the Grantham Institute at LSE[500], IPSO concluded – and the *Mail on Sunday* accepted[501] – that the article went substantially further in its claims than was justified by its source material, making 'assertions of fact that the data had been demonstrated conclusively to be wrong and had a significant impact on the decision making of world leaders, with an additional implication this had been part of a wilful attempt to deceive'. The *Mail on Sunday* subsequently admitted that two follow-up articles by David Rose on the initial NOAA story also contained serious errors, and made corrections.[502]

These two examples illustrate further the point that contrarianism has really run out of valid arguments. In straining to keep 'the debate' alive, it is increasingly pushing into territory that lies beyond the land of credibility. Since that hat-trick of articles in February 2017, the *Mail on Sunday* has published no further David Rose climate change 'exposés'.

A portion of the think-tank world is miring itself in similar sticky ground. Christmas 2016 saw the latest attempt to persuade us that the lights are going to go out because of the clean energy transition. The report, *Electric Shock*[503], came this time from the British Infrastructure Group (BIG), which professes to be a 'cross-party group of MPs dedicated to promoting better infrastructure in the UK'.[504] Its chair is former Conservative Party chairman Grant Shapps.

The report's headline claim was certainly striking – 'By next winter, the Christmas lights could go out'. And the group deployed a time-honoured PR tactic – circulating it to political correspondents rather than energy specialists, just a few hours before the embargo time, at what is a journalist's busiest time of year given the need to prepare seasonal features alongside reporting daily news, and – of course! – get to the best parties.

Initially it paid off. Scary headline, topical link to Christmas, higher bills, a well-known politician – an irresistible combination. It was duly written up by the *Times, Telegraph, Mail, Mirror* and *Sun*, and by the Press Association, the national news agency whose copy is syndicated to virtually every media outlet in the country.

On closer inspection the story began to smell as bad as a Christmas turkey left out in a warm kitchen for too long. The headline claim was obviously highly dubious, and based on a fundamental misunderstanding, accidental or deliberate, of National Grid figures: the report claimed the UK had only a 0.1 per cent 'safety margin' in generating capacity for the winter, when the true value was 6.6%. It was also clear that BIG's report contained nothing in the way of evidence.

The third point of contention was BIG itself. It transpired that the group has only one MP, Shapps, as a permanent affiliate. Others lend their name to certain projects; but to this one, none had. So rather than being a report from 'a cross-party group of MPs', it appeared that *Electric Shock* had but two authors – Grant Shapps and his researcher Tim Philpott. A possible clue to the report's genesis lay in a supporting quote contributed by Daniel Mahoney of the Centre for Policy Studies (CPS), a think-tank that has 'previous' on the 'lights going out' scare story – including having used the same erroneous 0.1 per cent capacity margin claim in a report it had published three months earlier.[505]

Matt Ridley also gave a supporting quote, to the effect that 'The lights will probably stay on this winter, but only just, and at exorbitant cost'[506] – although this has curiously vanished from the 'report' as it now stands on the BIG website.

After official complaints, all of the newspapers that had reported the story amended their online copy, and *The Sun* published a correction in a subsequent print edition. The Press Association took the extraordinary step of completely re-writing its original article and re-publishing – extraordinary because for a news agency, accuracy is a key currency, and mistakes of this magnitude are rarely made.

So, who won? BIG, Shapps and Philpott got their story printed. But no-one with any knowledge of the reality will have believed it; and all of those publications' editors are likely to look much more closely at any future claims that the lights are about to go out, especially those given support by the Centre for Policy Studies or other think-tanks that live close by.

Some in the environment movement lambast the UK media for what they see as misinformation on climate change and energy, and hold that large chunks of the industry are either incompetent or politically bent or both. I have little time for this line of argument.

Left-leaning people who mount tirade after tirade against the *Daily Mail* have little idea, I think, of the professionalism needed to make such publications as consistently appealing to readers as they are, day after day and week after week, in an increasingly competitive market. Similarly, anyone accusing BBC journalists of laziness has not a clue of the reality. And newspapers usually do care about accuracy – mostly before the fact, sometimes afterwards.

I have been involved twice in complaints about *Daily Mail* articles; on both occasions the paper engaged with considerable depth and was willing to front up and acknowledge errors. With very few exceptions, in the end, whatever the editor's and proprietor's worldview, credibility matters.

It was on exactly the point of credibility that, in April 2016, a group of 13 members of the House of Lords, including many with glittering track records in science, wrote a letter to *The Times* editor John Witherow.[507] Citing a number of contrarian-themed articles, the peers said that some of the paper's recent coverage risked bringing 'discredit on your paper' – a paper which, they noted, 'occupies a special place in the history of British journalism, with the best claim of any to having been the nation's newspaper of record'.

They suggested that 'many of the sub-standard news stories and opinion pieces appear to concern, in some way, GWPF', and asked whether the paper had allowed this small NGO to have 'a high degree of influence.'

Rather than responding itself, *The Times* allowed Matt Ridley to answer through his regular column on the following Monday.[508] Ridley attempted to turn it into a 'free speech' issue, even though the peers' had been clear that their intervention was not about free speech but about credibility. *The Times'* decision raised some interesting questions: was Ridley speaking for it, or on his own behalf? Was the decision proof of the peers' contention – that the paper allowed GWPF too much influence? His column was reproduced in its entirety on the GWPF website, which on the face of it is remarkable: *The Times* places its content behind a paywall, for commercial reasons – yet here was material from one of its highest-profile columnists being re-posted on a free-to-read third-party website, circumventing its paywall.[509]

One corollary of the decision was that *The Times* was obliged to print a right-of-reply letter from two of the peers, Lords Krebs and May, pointing out errors in Ridley's reading of the matter – in the process highlighting, in the paper's own pages, what they suggested might be an overly close relationship with GWPF.[510]

Ridley's columns aside, *The Times'* commentary on climate change and clean energy is now of a very different character. Not so that of The *Sunday Telegraph,* which continues to outsource a weekly column to Christopher Booker. And Booker himself re-outsources much of his content to a single blogger, Paul Homewood. In 2018, he twice based articles about possible links between climate change and US weather[511,512] on entries on Homewood's notalotofpeopleknowthat blog.[513,514] Two Homewood blog posts on Greenland's weather[515,516] were also recycled for the *Sunday Telegraph*'s readers[517,518], as was criticism of the Met Office for reporting that May 2018 was probably the UK's warmest on record.[519]

Over the preceding couple of years, Booker cites Homewood and his blog in columns about countries' pledges to the UN climate convention[520], the cost of decarbonising energy[521], and BBC coverage of electric motoring[522], in addition to more weather-related matters. Simon Evans of the *CarbonBrief* website – evidently on a slow news day! – calculated that Booker bases one in five *Sunday Telegraph* columns on Homewood's blog posts.[523]

By any standards, that is quite some reliance on a single source. And in those articles that I have read, I have not seen Booker display a shred of scepticism towards Homewood's calculations. As an aside, Homewood's professed position on climate change is that 'the sun controls the climate, and CO_2 is meaningless'.[524]

Booker's close relationship with Homewood and the *Telegraph's* apparent approval of it bring echoes of his previous association with Richard North. Which, as we saw earlier, did not end well, with the paper having to apologise to former IPCC chief Rajendra Pachauri for unfounded allegations and remove the offending article from its website. You might think that the dangers of another outsourcing operation would be obvious. But if anything, this association seems to be even stronger: according to Homewood, the *Telegraph* is also engaging him to advise on complaints against Booker's articles – which, given how many of them originate in Homewood's blogs, is surely the most circular and self-referential quality control mechanism you could ever invent.[525]

Homewood's closeness to Booker was illustrated again by a comment he posted on his own blog in February. The post was a diatribe against a *Telegraph* article on renewables by energy editor Jillian Ambrose.[526] 'I would suggest someone makes an official complaint,' he writes. 'I would, but I don't want to embarrass Booker'.

This particular comment leads on to another reason why contrarians are increasingly responsible for their own marginalisation.

In 2009, during the Copenhagen summit, *Sunday Times* columnist Charles Clover wrote an article noting that the contrarian interpretation of the emails hacked from the Universty of East Anglia 'has unleashed upon the rest of us the phenomenon of the born-again climate sceptic, the kind of man (always a man, almost invariably wearing a tweed jacket) who now materialises beside me at parties and confides that he has been having second thoughts about climate change'.[527]

I developed the theme in a BBC blog post in which I also noted that the meeting organised outside the Copenhagen summit by climate contrarians numbered not a single woman on its list of speakers.[528]

Clover had hit anecdotally on a conclusion borne out by research such as the 2009 'Six Americas' survey.[529] The 7 per cent of the US population most dismissive of climate change, they found, comprises twice as many men as women. Typically, they believe that climate change is not happening or that it has natural causes, or that there is a lot of disagreement among scientists. They feel very well-informed about the subject, and say they are unlikely to change their minds.

Today, the Global Warming Policy Foundation's Board of Trustees and Academic Advisory Council together number 36 men – and just one woman.[530,531] The group of contrarian commentators in the UK media also includes a single woman, Melanie Phillips – and she is not now a frequent writer on the issue. *The Spectator's* infamous pre-Paris Agreement 'special edition' featured not a single woman among the featured contrarians.

Why this might be is a question that would necessitate a whole other book. Suffice it to say that statistically, the odds of it occurring by chance are vanishingly small. But what is also undeniably true is that at least some prominent contrarian men have a problem treating women as equals.

This is doubly noticeable in an era when some of the UK's best energy journalism – traditionally the preserve of men – is being done by women. Jillian Ambrose, Emily Gosden at *The Times*, Nathalie Thomas and Sylvia Pfeifer at the *Financial Times* are among the finest journalists on the beat, and they are not alone. Their gender and age appear to be problems for some contrarians.

It certainly appears to be an issue for Paul Homewood and his supporters, among whom the widely-respected Gosden is dismissed as 'little Emily'. 'Dear little Emily does not get it, does she?', he opens a 2016 blog post.[532] After she moved from the *Telegraph* to *The Times*, he was equally outraged about her equally respected successor Jillian Ambrose who, he writes, 'seems just as soppy'.[533]

Commenters on his blog seem quite happy with this tone of discourse. One suggests that neither journalist would know the difference between a combined-cycle and an open-cycle gas turbine (CCGT and OCGT) and would 'probably think it's something to do with gin and tonic.' Another recalls former *Telegraph* environment correspondent Louise Gray, and suggests that all three are 'jejeune ladies' who 'don't do techie stuff'.[534] On another post, Homewood weighs in on *Telegraph* columnist Lucy Mangan, dismissing her as a 'silly little girl.'[535]

Nigel Lawson has not been above such comments himself, referring in 2014 to Dame Julia Slingo, one of the UK's most decorated climate scientists and at the time Met Office Chief Scientist, as 'just this Julia Slingo woman'.[536] To James Delingpole of Breitbart News, the equally decorated Professor Joanna Haigh of Imperial College London, until recently the Royal Society's scientific lead on climate change, is a 'puffed-up missy', and Dr Emily Shuckburgh, Head of Open Oceans at the British Antarctic Survey, 'some foxy chick'.[537,538]

Given that Breitbart's most notorious fan is Donald Trump, perhaps one should not be surprised that Delingpole feels able to go there; but one might hope for better from a peer of the Realm.[539bb]

More recently Sir Christopher Chope, one of the three MPs to vote against the Climate Change Act in 2008 and who still asserts that the Act is 'a very extreme measure... totally inconsistent with our long-term economic interests', used arcane parliamentary procedure to block a bill that would have made upskirting a criminal offence.[540,541] It is not clear that he understood what it is, let along its salience with at least half of the population. Perhaps he should have asked his Prime Minister about both upskirting and climate change, given that she is clearly much better informed than he about both.

Why this male corner of climate and energy discourse should hold half of the human race in such apparent disregard is not clear to me. However, a clue appeared in a comment posted on my BBC blog from Copenhagen – the blog highlighting the over-representation of men in the contrarian community. The person commenting – a man, I presume – suggested it was because men were more intelligent than women and were thus better able to spot holes in the edifice of climate science. It was apparently made seriously.

Though other contrarians might privately be appalled by all of this, none, to my knowledge, has called out his fellow travellers.

[bb] The tendency is not limited to the UK. Canadian Environment Minister Catherine McKenna is regularly derided by opponents as 'climate Barbie', including by former opposition MP Gerry Ritz

Whatever the reasons behind it, it is surely abundantly clear that such attitudes will win you few friends. As a strategy for gaining kudos in the twenty-first century, belittling women is as poor as it gets.

If climate contrarianism is disappearing as a serious influence in the UK – and it is this book's thesis that it is – then the factors outlined above are surely among those responsible. The real world is one in which evidence of man-made climate change and its attendant risks emerges daily, as does evidence of the changing economics of energy and the public's support for decarbonisation. Both are highly visible. Only a small group of people, it seems, chooses to block this out and – in many cases – claim that the facts are otherwise.

As I have outlined above, this is increasingly being noted, both in politics and the media. Ministers, back-bench MPs, editors and writers are eschewing contrarianism and its proponents for credibility and relevance. Increasingly, the contrarian establishment finds itself the butt of the sort of ridicule that no individual nor organisation with serious pretensions would want to invite.

After *The Spectator* published a particularly strange article in 2014, a group of young activists took out a spoof advert on a jobs website, seeking a fact-checker for the magazine's climate change and energy coverage.[542] During the Paris summit, a spoof memo was published on the internet from

'Benny' – presumably a reference to GWPF director Benny Peiser – to a group of recipients including 'Charles M', 'Chris B', 'Matt R', 'Quentin L' and 'James D', advising on 'lines to take' during forthcoming articles.[543]

'Global temperatures are NOT RISING,' was one of the suggested lines. 'Only satellites can measure temperatures, and the satellite record shows no warming. Thermometers are useless: DO NOT MENTION THERMOMETERS WHEN TALKING ABOUT THE TEMPERATURE.' Another suggested line to take is: 'Energy bills will rise, industries will flee the country, and "the lights will go out"... invoke the Four Horsemen or Judgement Day if you feel it appropriate'. *Spectator* chairman Andrew Neil was thanked for having 'loaned' the magazine out to GWPF the week previously for its collection of anti-Paris Summit articles.

At times, newspapers' other columnists have joined in the ribbing. I noted Hugo Rifkind's *Spectator* letter earlier, but how about this from David Aaronovitch in *The Times* in 2016:[544]

> 'When it comes to fear, prejudice, poor science, confirmation bias and conspiracism, few lobbies can match the anti-man-made-climate-change brigade. The overwhelming scientific consensus, including from those most expert in the field, is that carbon dioxide emissions lead to global warming, that we are responsible for a significant proportion of this phenomenon, and that, within a range, the consequences will be severe. But there is a voluble and powerful lobby (step forward Lord Lawson of

Blaby and most of the US Republican party) dedicated to the business of getting the rest of us to join them in jamming our fingers in our ears and singing *Nymphs and Shepherds* at the top of our voices.'

Contrarians seem resigned to the fact that in both the media and politics, the game is up. In August, following the *Daily Mail's* publication of an article by Lord (Michael) Howard highlighting the links between climate change and extreme weather[545], James Delingpole mourned: 'The fact that so rigorous and robust a newspaper should publish such dross is worrying indeed... If the *Mail* is now going to duck its responsibilities, that leaves only the *Sunday Telegraph* (not the embarrassingly pro-wind *Daily*) and the *Sun* in Britain's mainstream media prepared to tell the truth about the great climate con.'[546]

Paul Homewood spluttered: 'It appears that the *Mail* have (*sic*) given up any pretence of balance as far as climate change is concerned.'[547] 'Environmentalism is now the official religion of the Conservative Party,' complained Rupert Darwall earlier in the year.[548]

They are right to be concerned. The bridgehead that climate contrarianism built to such startling effect in the British media a decade ago opened the doors of ministers' offices and broadcasting studios with a frequency unthinkable to their opponents in the 'green' movement. It bestowed on some a public profile that brought book deals and lecture tours. It persisted long beyond the time and with far more prominence than were ever justified by its dwindling relationship with evidence or by its social legitimacy.

But for a variety of reasons, its time is indeed ending. When *Daily Telegraph* assistant editor Philip Johnston can observe that 'Margaret Thatcher was right' to warn us 30 years ago about the risks of climate change and call for a UN treaty[549] – when a *Times* editorial highlights the fact that that the UK's 25-year history of decarbonisation 'demonstrates that environmental policies and economic enrichment are compatible. Some corporate lobbyists have in the past doubted this and should not have done'[550] – when the *Daily Mail* says of energy bill hikes that 'Green levies are NOT to blame'[551] – when Conservative MPs from veteran Bernard Jenkin[552] to 2017 freshman Simon Clarke[553] laud the Climate Change Act and call for Britain to set a net zero emissions target in line with the Paris Agreement – the party is indeed over.

If one reason why is the sheer weight of evidence, another is the absolute lack of public interest in contrarian positions. There has been a campaign group in existence for years now which aims, as its name states, to Repeal the Act. You have almost certainly never heard of it – which speaks to just how unsuccessful it has been. In 2013, it posted a petition on the 10 Downing St website calling for the Act to be repealed or suspended and the Committee on Climate Change abolished. Over six months, it received the grand total of 1,720 signatures.[554]

A year ago, GWPF launched a petition on the change.org website to 'scrap expensive EU renewable targets.'[555] To date it has garnered 1,863 signatures. Six times as many people signed a petition on change.org calling for protection of the

War Memorial at Stoke-on-Trent's Town Hall.[556] Thirty-eight times more people want to prevent relocation of the skateboarding park on the South Bank of the Thames in London than back GWPF's call to scrap EU renewable energy targets.[557]

That, Nick Robinson, is the true size of the voice that you feel so strongly should be heard. Outside a tiny group of the political and media elite, the reality is that no-one cares. The next time that your editor Sarah Sands picks up the phone to book a guest for the Today Programme, perhaps she would reflect her audience's interests better by skipping past Nigel Lawson's number and instead inviting one of the South Bank's displaced skateboarders to air their grievances.

There is still a piece of the jigsaw missing: exactly how and why have the dwindling group of contrarians taken the path that they have?

A group that ten years ago was highly relevant to the public and political discourse – which shaped opinions, steered politics and commanded a sizeable media platform – how have they allowed themselves to walk off into the twilight?

A clue lies in a favoured contrarian narrative: that everyone concerned with climate change and clean energy has been captured by 'group-think', and only a few special people can see through it.

This is a contention that one sees explicitly from time to time in contrarian articles and which implicitly lies at the heart of many more. Witness

David Rose's article on the NOAA temperature record, whose thesis can perhaps best be summarised as: 'The institutions of science and the global body politic were taken in by this paper – but I saw through it'. Or the over-hyping of small modular nuclear reactors: 'They might not actually exist as a commercial entity, but I know they'll be cheaper than renewables.'

Christopher Booker recently laid out the argument in a report written for GWPF entitled *Global Warming: A Case Study in Group Think*.[558] Booker draws on the work of Yale psychologist Irving Janis to argue that the scientific, economic, social and political case for decarbonisation is, in fact, just group-think, with those arguing for it convinced that they 'just know', without engaging in rational thought or real debate.

Booker is not alone: Matt Ridley has also said that his takeaway from his disastrous time as chair of the Northern Rock Building Society was that never again would he fall prey to 'group-think'.[559]

We have met Christopher Booker many times already in these pages, so it will not come as a surprise to learn that his report wins no prizes for accuracy. As a small example, he mentions me twice, bestowing on me two different BBC job titles, neither of which I actually held. More important inaccuracies jump out too – for example, a contention that carbon capture and storage was in 2011 'a technology not even yet developed', when the capture technology has been in existence since the 1930s and a large commercial sub-seabed storage facility in operation since 1996.[560,561]

There are many more. When he writes of the Paris Agreement that: 'The rest of the world, led by the fast-growing economies of China and India, has made clear that, whatever the West may continue to believe or do, it is carrying on [growing emissions] regardless', he has evidently missed both China's pledge to peak its carbon emissions by 2030 and its massive ongoing investment in clean energy and transportation.[562]

Despite the inaccuracies, I find myself agreeing with some of Booker's propositions. Environment groups have sometimes been too keen to link extreme weather events to climate change without always waiting for formal scientific attribution. Politicians such as Tony Blair and David Cameron have donned the 'green' mantle when it suited them and discarded it when it did not. Some scientists were too keen to proclaim a decade ago that 'the science is settled', at a time when science lacked an explanation for the apparent global warming slowdown.

But the report's real insight lies in what it reveals about contrarian thought. It is exemplified in the passage in which Booker disallows the notion that anyone who believes climate change to be a significant problem can have reached that position through critical analysis.

> 'When we come to consider the story of the belief in man-made global warming, we are of course looking at how this was shared by countless other people: academics, politicians, the media, teachers, business executives, indeed public opinion in general.

'But all these people only got carried along by the belief that manmade global warming was real and dangerous because they had been told it was so by others. They accepted as true what they had heard, read or just seen on television without questioning it. And this meant that they didn't really know why they thought what they did. They hadn't thought it necessary to give such a complicated and technical subject any fundamental study. They simply echoed what had been passed on to them from somewhere else, usually in the form of a few familiar arguments or articles of belief that were, like approved mantras, endlessly repeated.'

And there you have the position at which contrarians have arrived in a nutshell. 'I think Y, while the vast majority of people think X. I have come to my own conclusion and I know that I am right; so logically anyone who disagrees with me must be falling prey to group-think.'

Doubtless there are plenty of people concerned about man-made climate change who have not examined the science themselves, but who accept that when all of the world's science academies, every government and even the oil industry endorses the evidence, there is probably something to it. But many others, in academia, politics, business and journalism *have* examined the evidence – especially those in businesses and governments for which an end to fossil fuel use presents an existential crisis – and have just come to the opposite conclusion from Chris Booker.

The thing most conspicuously absent from Booker's analysis is, of course, a mirror. Booker writes reports for GWPF: Matt Ridley uses his newspaper column to promote GWPF reports: Ridley cites Bjorn Lomborg's economic analysis to support his own; Lomborg writes a hagiographic article about Ridley's favoured global greening; GWPF promotes Lomborg's columns; GWPF chair Lawson's book is promoted by GWPF trustee Charles Moore; Booker cites Homewood's blog, Homewood features Booker's articles, Delingpole recycles the top lines, GWPF posts Delingpole's articles... and so on and so on, round and round in a self-regarding circle of ever-shrinking circumference, one tiny conversation within a tiny group that has detached itself from the real world.

It has locked the door on external scrutiny and discourse, disallowing anything that runs counter to its views, never stopping to turn any of its loudly-trumpeted scepticism on itself and consider that some of its core beliefs might be disproven.

This was not the first time that Booker had made the 'group-think' argument. It is a thread that runs through his 2009 book *The Real Global Warming Disaster*. And it is equally clear that then too a mirror was lacking. In the book's concluding 'personal note', Booker namechecks people who shaped his views on climate change. Veteran US contrarian Fred Singer, Ian Plimer, Myron Ebell of the Competitive Enterprise Institute, Anthony Watts – pretty much all of the movers and shakers in the contrarian world of the 2000s are reflected here, as they are in the references for Booker's source material.

What there is no sign of is even a single encounter with a mainstream climate scientist. Nor yet with an investor in the field of renewable energy, an electric car engineer, or anyone from an impacted region of the world such as the Arctic or the Pacific. No women, no young people, no-one with a 'real job'. No diversity at all. An account, absolutely, of how group-think happens.

The irony is that in the world of science, one finds independent thought in abundance. Climate science and energy policy are overflowing with real and feisty arguments, whether over the disappearance date for Arctic summer sea-ice or the optimal decarbonisation pathway for household heating. Within civil society, there are equally powerful conversations raging right now about how emission reductions should be assigned between nations, how 'negative emissions' approaches can be done in ways that are good for indigenous peoples and wildlife, about intensive vs non-intensive agriculture.

If no-one is seriously engaging with the contrarian community any more, it is not because the rest of the world is suffering from group-think – it is because contrarianism has so isolated itself from evidence-based dialogue as to contribute very little of any value.

As Booker writes, apparently without irony:

> 'Those possessed by group-think were convinced that they just "knew" what it was they thought they knew. They were used to talking about it only to those who shared the same beliefs. They were incapable of focussing properly on any evidence that might seem to contradict their certainties.'

Well – indeed.

In the third week of April 2018, the UK hosted

the biennial Commonwealth Heads of Government meeting (CHOGM) in London. On the Monday of that week, ITV broadcast a conversation between the Queen and Sir David Attenborough.

As they strolled through the sun-dappled glades of the Buckingham Palace gardens, the two nonagenarian icons – two of the most trusted people in Britain[563] – spoke with understated passion about their common concern for the world's wildlife, its forests, and the issue of climate change.[564]

The same week, New Zealand's young and heavily pregnant Prime Minister Jacinda Ardern wrote of her determination to constrain climate change for future generations.[565] Sweden's Deputy Prime Minister Isabella Lövin, whose cabinet had so memorably trolled Donald Trump in an all-female photoshoot months beforehand,[566] detailed why her nation has already enacted a law that will phase out its net greenhouse gas emissions within a single generation.[567] Buoyed by an opinion survey showing that three-quarters of Britons support a similar move,[568] the government announced that it would commission a formal review of the UK's 2050 climate target, which is likely to result in that target being set at net zero emissions.[569]

In the same week, but very much in a parallel world, Rupert Darwall was dismissing wind energy, Britons' second-favourite form of electricity generation, on the grounds that the Nazis had once supported it.[570]

There could be no clearer illustration of the irrelevance into which climate contrarians have written themselves. And no starker illustration of why they have lost.

Epilogia

Choices, 1

There are two possible ways forward for climate contrarians: business-as-usual, or evolution.

Business-as-usual will involve, first, a number of reactions to this book. One is that I will be personally attacked on social media – the man being played rather than the ball. Perhaps Christopher Booker or James Delingpole will do me the honour, in the absence of Black's Whitewash, of – er – blackwashing me in a column. Fortunately, the one thing I know I do not have to fear is a legal suit, given the contrarians' unwavering support for free speech.

Somewhere in this book, despite my fact-checking and that of my kind reviewers, there is probably an error; under business-as-usual, this will be highlighted and repeated *ad nauseam,* and the claim made that it undermines the whole book. Perhaps there will be more than one.

More importantly, under business-as-usual we will see the same set of arguments advanced by the same set of columnists, with *The Spectator* treating us to the occasional omnibus edition. They will be interlaced with familiar pieces of whataboutery – the glacier that grows, the new scientific paper that proves climate sensitivity to be low, the wind farm facing vehement community opposition, the month when Arctic sea ice 'recovers'. The outcome will, inevitably, be the same: the credibility of columnist and publication will sink a little further. Contrarians will continue to lobby the BBC with the same canonical arguments, claiming that public opinion is the opposite of what it actually is. All the while, public opinion will stubbornly refuse to do what it is told.

The House of Lords will continue to reverberate with occasional denunciations of wind farms, and the Economic Affairs Committee will periodically find new ways of trying to oppose the overwhelming will of the people by outlining new arguments against decarbonisation. Perhaps the newly-enobled Peter Lilley will cite in the House of Lords as he once did in the Commons the presence of snow in Westminster as evidence that climate change is not so serious.

Business-as-usual will presumably bring a certain set of rewards; but if it is the path of least resistance, it is also the path guaranteeing least relevance.

There is another way, along which the leading contrarians can steer their community if they choose. And that is to re-engage with reality – to evolve discredited arguments rapidly, coming up to date with where the science is (in its totality), where business is, where the public is. The starting-point is to accept the conclusion implicit in both Christopher Booker's GWPF report and in the community's increasingly manifest lack of credibility and traction, and renounce those canonical arguments that have clearly had their day. No-one ever died from admitting they were wrong.

To continue as things are would be an absolute waste of some fine minds. There are real questions on which the casting of a genuinely sceptical eye would be a boon: indeed, the highlighting of problems with biomass use in power generation shows that occasionally, contrarians do still home in on real issues. So, having examined whether biomass's credentials are genuinely low-carbon, how about asking the same question of shale gas? Or probing the corporate lobbying operation around SMRs?

On a macro-scale, there are questions about how the UK moves to low-carbon home heating that are far more interesting and profound than tired diatribes against a 'broken' energy market. There are genuine connections to energy poverty and regional development. Meanwhile decentralisation of power generation offers opportunities for innovation, for the challenging of stale models of complacent corporate incumbency, and the establishment of local markets, which ought logically to appeal to anyone in a pro-free-market think-tank.

Engaging with the questions of 2018 rather than attempting to keep those of 2008 alive would be a route back to relevance and credibility. I, for one, hope the leading lights of the contrarian community take it. But I am not holding my breath.

Red flags

One of the reasons why climate and energy 'scepticism' retained traction for so long is due, somewhat ironically, to a lack of scepticism in parts of politics and journalism.

Here, to aid scepticism, are five phrases and memes that should all act as 'red flags' – signalling at least a need to check the veracity of the statement being made, and at most that the person making it may be either ill-informed or disingenuous.

1. *The energy market (as in 'Britain's energy market is broken')*

Britain has many energy markets. Even within the electricity sector (where the 'broken' meme is usually deployed) there are four separate national markets: for wholesale electricity, capacity, low-carbon generation (Contracts for Difference) and ancillary services. This is just at the top level: the wholesale market involves a whole suite of different trading possibilities, from years ahead to spot, while ancillary services are an entire rabbit hole in themselves. There is an international market, with power being bought and sold through the cables that connect the UK with the rest of Europe, and local markets are starting to emerge too.

Then there is gas, which again is traded effectively in several markets with lead times ranging from years to hours ahead. And there are markets too for fuels such as coal and biomass.

The 'energy market is broken' phrase is usually used by people who would prefer an instant return to a wholesale-only market in the electricity sector. There are undoubtedly issues with the current structure of electricity markets (note plural). But a wholesale-only market could never drive a transition to a system based on low-carbon generation with flexibility mechanisms, plus grid-strengthening and grid-smartening, which is needed to meet carbon targets and desirable for many other reasons including reducing reliance on fuel imports, lowering bills and democratising the current industry oligarchy. It was somewhat ironic to see commentators such as Andrew Neil blaming the gas supply crunch during the March 2018 'Beast from the East' on government interference in 'the energy market' given that gas markets are as free as can be.

So if you hear the phrase 'the energy market', first ask the question: 'which market'? And then ask, given the structural change needed both to bring carbon emissions down and to take full advantage of emerging smart technologies, what system would work better than the one we have now, under which both emissions and bills are falling while security of supply increases?

2. *Energy prices (as in 'energy prices are soaring')*

Customers do not pay prices; they – we – pay bills. As a customer it makes no difference to me whether my bill has fallen because the unit price of energy has fallen or because I am using fewer units in my better-insulated home: either way, my bill has gone down, and I am happy.

Overall, unit prices of electricity have risen over the last decade. But the average energy bill has shrunk despite the rising amount of renewable generation funded through bills. It has shrunk because we are each using less energy – partly due to efficiency improvements also funded through bills. Therefore, contrarian commentators who dislike the transition to clean energy usually choose to highlight price changes only.

So, if you see a claim about rising energy prices – particularly if it is preceded by the word 'crippling' – check what is happening to bills. Bills are affected by network costs and company profits, as well as by wholesale costs, levies and usage. They may go up and they may go down – but changes in unit prices will not be the only factor.

3. Baseline years matter

As I have shown twice in this book, misleading narratives can be created through the effective selection of a starting year. Construction of the 'ten-year global warming pause' narrative relied on the choice of El Niño-enhanced 1998 for the starting year. Unsurprisingly, when El Niño conditions ebbed away, the global temperature fell.

The second example is the choice by Dieter Helm in his 2017 Cost of Energy Review, and by the House of Lords Economic Affairs Committee in its report issued earlier in the year, of 2003 and 2004 as the starting years for energy price comparisons – years when the wholesale gas price was abnormally low, hence producing the highest possible number for the subsequent rise in energy prices.

So, if someone gives you a historical comparison – X has become Y times more/less likely/expensive since the year Z – see whether Z has been chosen to give a particular impression, and ask what happens when you begin in the years either side of Z, rather than in Z itself.

4. In decarbonisation, timescale matters

'Clean gas is a bridging fuel...' 'Small modular reactors are a better bet than windfarms...' even 'Coal can be a part of Britain's clean energy future...'

There is a famous phrase about climate change: 'To succeed too slowly is to fail'. Science sets a timescale on which emissions must be reduced and eliminated if governments are to meet given targets, such as those in the Paris Agreement or in national legislation. It is on this basis that the UK Climate Change Act's long-term target is to cut emissions by at least 80 per cent by 2050 – not by 2060, or some indeterminate point in the future.

The government says that by 2032 – just 14 years after this book's publication – only about 15 per cent of our electricity should come from unabated gas-fired power stations and other high-carbon sources such as small diesel generators.[571]

Currently, gas-fired power stations generate about 40 per cent of our electricity in 2017 – coal just 7 per cent.[572] The targeted decline in coal-fired generation between now and the phase-out date of 2025 is thus one percentage point per year; for gas-fired generation, from now until 2032, it is two percentage points per year. So, if gas is to be a 'bridge to a low-carbon future' in the power sector, it is clearly a very short bridge.

A similar point goes for SMRs and other as yet non-existent generation technologies. Yes, they may emerge, they may be cost-effective, the public may grow to love them, they may have a significant role to play in the expansion of generation that will be needed post-2030 to power electric transportation. But they will not be a reality for at least a decade, by the admission of companies in the sector. So they cannot play a meaningful role in obtaining 85 per cent of our electricity from low-carbon sources by 2030. For that, the only games in town are the tried and tested methods of renewables, large nuclear reactors and the four flexibility mechanisms (including peaking gas-fired plant) that go alongside them – alongside reducing demand and waste.

So, for every claim that such-and-such a technology is better than those we have, a question to ask is – how quickly can it be here?

5. 'We should,' 'we must'

Most often encountered with fracking and shale gas – 'we should get on with shale gas now', 'we must get fracking' – this simple phrase hides a crucial question: who is 'we'?

If Britain ever develops a shale gas industry, it will be in the private sector. So by 'we', presumably, proponents really mean 'companies'. In that case, why not say so – 'Cuadrilla should get fracking', or 'BP ought to be extracting shale oil'? Presumably such statements would receive short shrift, as Parliamentarians or newspaper columnists generally have no business telling private companies how to run themselves.

So does 'we' mean government? The 'we should'

phrase generally comes from people who abhor state ownership of assets – so are they advocating, here, state ownership – 'the government should itself get fracking'? It seems unlikely. Which presumably means, therefore, 'adjusting, adjusting again and adjusting financial and planning incentives' – if you prefer, 'rigging, rigging and rigging the market' – until companies are satiated.

But hang on – is this not what governments have historically done with wind farms and solar panels? And has this not brought criticism from those very commentators who now promote shale gas, on the basis that 'governments should not pick winners'?

The same point arises on a global scale. To return for a moment to the argument that 'Africa should' expand coal-fired electricity generation – who exactly is meant by Africa? Who is supposed to be the agent who 'should' make it happen – and with whose money? Unless that is answered, the argument is hollow at source.

For a columnist or peer to say 'we should get fracking' or 'we should invest in SMRs' or 'Africa should do this or that' is an easy phrase. It creates the idea that some entity is not doing what it can and should. It is always a phrase worth opening up, and asking the proponent: 'who is "we" – and why should they?'

Choices, 2

Climate scientists do not predict the future. What they do – as do national scientific advisors and the Intergovernmental Panel on Climate Change – is to map out ranges of possible futures based on the best information available at the time. Those ranges may or may not turn out to be correct, but they are the best estimates currently available – based on real-world evidence, collated and analysed by the people best qualified to do so.

It is then up to us, as a global civilisation, to make choices. Governments' actions have more impact than those of businesses, and both have more effect than individuals' life-style choices. But ultimately both governments and businesses must, in most nations, respond to the will of their peoples.

I will be confident in predicting that we will follow neither of the pathways proffered at extreme ends of the political spectrum: we will not continue increasing greenhouse gas emissions at the rate seen in the 90s and noughties, nor will we follow the Naomi Klein prescription of overthrowing capitalism. Enlightened self-interest and the realities of business mitigate against the former; and as for the latter – well, as John Lennon observed: 'If you go carrying pictures of Chairman Mao, You ain't going to make it with anyone anyhow.'

People from Bradford to Bangkok generally like capitalism as a system and enjoy what it gives us, if not always its excesses; and if carbon emissions are to be reduced on a timescale compatible with the Paris Agreement targets, world revolution is not an option.

Within the structures of current politics, then, the choices we make in the next few years are going to be critical. If governments, businesses and citizens are serious about constraining climate change within boundaries that some consider 'safe', whether that is 2°C or 1.5°C, a lot of changes are needed quickly. They include rapid adoption of low-carbon energy and a step-change in how efficiently we use it. They include global co-operation to help the poorest countries leap-frog the fossil fuel era, and policymaking that prioritises the next generation alongside our own.

Above all and most urgently, they involve stopping doing the 'stupid stuff' – ramping down the use of coal as soon as possible, abandoning plans to open new oil- and coal-fields, stopping building poorly-insulated homes, ending net deforestation. All stuff, incidentally, that we know how to do.

If all that happens and humanity gets lucky – if climate sensitivity turns out to be low-ish and the natural world does not start releasing greenhouse gases from drying forests and melting tundra as it warms – there is a fair chance of delivering on the Paris Agreement. That in turn will mean that climate change impacts can be kept for the most part below levels that while absolutely not 'safe' for all societies and ecosystems are likely to be manageable for most.

Not making those changes on the timescale required is likely to usher in a rather different future, of greater climate change impacts on people and nature – more floods, more drought, more sea-level rise, greater losses in crop yields, more heat-related health effects, more damage to the natural world. It raises the risk of turning both known and unknown unknowns into realities. We cannot know precisely the temperature rise at which irreversible processes such as melting of the polar ice-sheets kick in – but science shows it is eminently possible at levels of global warming that we may soon be experiencing.

Peaking global emissions by 2020, halving them by

2030 and eliminating them by mid-century, which the IPCC concludes is necessary to have a chance of keeping global warming to 1.5°C, are challenging targets. But they appear to be eminently achievable, given what humanity has already proven itself capable of in the decarbonisation field. There is no mystery to cutting energy waste, nor to building solar panels and nuclear reactors. Countries in all stages of development have already trimmed agricultural emissions by adopting minimum-till farming methods. China and India are both pressing hard on electric transportation, which will inevitably drive it forwards elsewhere. Nowhere are these transformations leading to poverty, while developing nations from giant China to tiny Samoa are deriving additional benefits through cleaning up their air and reducing reliance on fuel imports.

Of course, you do not have to accept this picture, based though it is on the assembled expertise of the world's best-qualified scientists, naturalists, energy academics and practitioners, and on what is happening on the ground in countries from the Equator to the poles. There is, as there always has been, 'another side to the story' – and I fully anticipate that some will continue telling it, despite the fact that it is diverging ever more glaringly from reality.

In September 1988, Prime Minister Margaret Thatcher told Britain's illustrious Royal Society that humanity had 'unwittingly begun a massive experiment with the system of this planet itself'.[573] Thirty years on, results of that experiment are flooding in; and from the tropics to the poles, from the bottom of the ocean to the stratosphere, they show that she was basically right.

Climate change is very much a reality, and poses increasingly serious risks the further it progresses.

Fortunately, 30 years of human progress since Mrs Thatcher's speech also show that humanity has the tools to bring the experiment to an end – to constrain those risks – if we collectively choose to do so. We know how to slash carbon emissions in most sectors of the economy and end them completely in some. Where there are gaps in the knowledge, the overwhelming lessons of the last decades are that innovation combined with evidence-based policymaking delivers, and usually at far lower cost than forecast.

It is, fundamentally, all about choice.

References

[1]https://www.conservativehome.com/thinktankcentral/2017/11/sam-hall-environmental-policy-can-help-conservatives-win-over-younger-voters.html

[2] https://reutersinstitute.politics.ox.ac.uk/our-research/poles-apart

[3] https://www.gov.uk/government/publications/measles-confirmed-cases/confirmed-cases-of-measles-mumps-and-rubella-in-england-and-wales-2012-to-2013

[4] https://www.nursingtimes.net/news/latest/measles-vaccination-warning-amid-spate-of-european-outbreaks/7025669.article

[5]https://www.ncbi.nlm.nih.gov/pmc/articles/PMC1851707/#B11

[6] http://cdn2.sph.harvard.edu/wp-content/uploads/sites/47/2015/06/Lost_Benefits.pdf

[7] Paul Flynn, *Good as You: From Prejudice to Pride – 30 Years of Gay Britain*

[8]http://reutersinstitute.politics.ox.ac.uk/sites/default/files/research/files/Poles%2520Apart%2520the%2520international%2520reporting%2520of%2520climate%2520scepticism.pdf – drawing on an earlier analysis by Stefan Rahmstorf

[9]http://webarchive.loc.gov/all/20061225193018/http://www.g8.gov.uk/servlet/Front?pagename=OpenMarket/Xcelerate/ShowPage&c=Page&cid=1119518698846

[10]http://webarchive.nationalarchives.gov.uk/+/http://www.hm-treasury.gov.uk/sternreview_index.htm

[11] https://www.ipcc.ch/report/ar4/

[12]http://news.bbc.co.uk/1/shared/bsp/hi/pdfs/25_09_07climatepoll.pdf

[13]
https://www.instituteforgovernment.org.uk/sites/default/files/climate_change_act.pdf

[14] https://www.metoffice.gov.uk/hadobs/hadcrut4/

[15] https://www.telegraph.co.uk/comment/personal-view/3624242/There-IS-a-problem-with-global-warming...-it-stopped-in-1998.html

[16]http://blogs.nature.com/climatefeedback/2008/05/decade_break_in_global_warming.html

[17] See for example - http://www.bbc.co.uk/blogs/theeditors/2007/11/climate_sceptics.html - not all of the articles appear still to be online

[18]https://www.theguardian.com/environment/2009/oct/19/gordon-brown-copenhagen-climate-talks

[19] https://www.smh.com.au/environment/rudd-set-for-copenhagen-climate-change-summit-20091113-icva.html

[20] https://www.reuters.com/article/us-climate-copenhagen-idUSGEE5BB07F20091217

[21] http://enb.iisd.org/vol12/enb12459e.html

[22]https://www.tandfonline.com/doi/abs/10.1080/10220461.2011.622945?src=recsys&journalCode=rsaj20

[23] https://www.reuters.com/article/us-climate-denmark-negotiator-idUSTRE59B41T20091012

[24]https://www.theguardian.com/environment/2009/dec/08/copenhagen-climate-summit-disarray-danish-text

[25] http://news.bbc.co.uk/1/hi/8345501.stm

[26] http://news.bbc.co.uk/1/hi/8370282.stm

[27] https://www.thegwpf.org/who-we-are/

[28] https://www.thegwpf.org/lord-lawson-calls-for-public-inquiry-into-uea-global-warming-data-manipulation/

[29] https://www.thetimes.co.uk/article/copenhagen-will-fail-and-quite-right-too-hzffcs80c5d

[30]https://www.telegraph.co.uk/comment/columnists/christopherbooker/6679082/Climate-change-this-is-the-worst-scientific-scandal-of-our-generation.html

[31] https://www.express.co.uk/comment/columnists/neil-hamilton/143154/The-great-global-warming-con

[32] The article is no longer on the National Post website but is archived at http://climaterealists.com/index.php?id=4518

[33]https://en.wikipedia.org/wiki/Conrad_Black#Fraud_conviction

[34]http://science.sciencemag.org/content/326/5955/924.full?rss=1

[35] http://news.bbc.co.uk/1/hi/8387737.stm

[36] http://news.bbc.co.uk/1/hi/8392611.stm

[37] http://news.bbc.co.uk/1/hi/8426835.stm

[38] https://www.reuters.com/article/us-climate-copenhagen/china-unveils-carbon-target-for-copenhagen-deal-idUSTRE5AP11H20091126

[39] https://en.wikipedia.org/wiki/Plug-in_electric_vehicles_in_Norway

[40] http://www.cgd.ucar.edu/staff/trenbert/emails/

[41]https://en.wikipedia.org/wiki/The_Real_Global_Warming_Disaster

[42] https://www.nature.com/articles/nature06921

[43]http://www.pnas.org/content/early/2011/06/27/1102467108

[44] This wording appeared in the print edition of the Express above this article https://www.express.co.uk/comment/expresscomment/141453/Climate-change-The-most-costly-scientific-blunder-in-history - the wording is not the same in the online version. The original can be found through searching in a cuttings database such as Factiva

[45] https://www.metoffice.gov.uk/learning/ocean/el-nino

[46] https://www.ncdc.noaa.gov/teleconnections/pdo/

[47] https://climatedataguide.ucar.edu/climate-data/atlantic-multi-decadal-oscillation-amo

[48] http://www.wmo.int/pages/prog/wcp/ccl/faqs.php

[49] http://www.ipcc.ch/pdf/assessment-report/ar5/wg2/ar5_wgII_spm_en.pdf

[50] https://www.ncdc.noaa.gov/cag/global/time-series

[51] https://data.giss.nasa.gov/gistemp/

[52]http://ds.data.jma.go.jp/tcc/tcc/products/gwp/temp/ann_wld.html

[53] http://berkeleyearth.org

[54] http://www.ipcc.ch/report/ar5/wg1/

[55] https://nca2014.globalchange.gov/highlights/report-findings/our-changing-climate

[56] http://nsidc.org/arcticseaicenews/

[57] https://www.youtube.com/watch?v=6sbBxECIKxs

[58] http://www.sciencemag.org/news/2017/02/great-greenland-meltdown

[59] http://www.antarcticglaciers.org/2018/06/mass-balance-antarctic-ice-sheet-1992-2017/

[60] https://wgms.ch/downloads/WGMS_GGCB_02.pdf

[61] https://science2017.globalchange.gov/chapter/12/

[62] https://www.nature.com/articles/nclimate2513

[63] https://floats.pmel.noaa.gov

[64]https://www.pmel.noaa.gov/co2/story/What+is+Ocean+Acidification%3F

[65]http://lajeunesse.myweb.usf.edu/papers/Cohen_Lajeunesse_Rohr_2018_Nature_Climate_Change.pdf

[66]http://www.theurbanclimatologist.com/uploads/4/4/2/5/44250401/hicklingetal2006insectsfishpoleward.pdf

[67]http://aura.abdn.ac.uk/bitstream/handle/2164/7914/270166_6_merged_1464271961.pdf?sequence=1&isAllowed=y

[68]http://ro.uow.edu.au/cgi/viewcontent.cgi?article=5654&context=smhpapers

[69]http://www.sfu.ca/biology/faculty/jwmoore/teaching/REM475/Chen_etal_Science_2011.pdf

[70] http://marinepalaeoecology.org/wp-content/uploads/2011/09/nclimate1958.pdf

[71] https://www.spectator.co.uk/2017/03/hot-air/

[72] https://www.nationalreview.com/2016/05/climate-change-attorneys-general/

[73]Shttps://www.independent.co.uk/news/world/americas/us-politics/james-bridenstine-nasa-climate-change-denier-donald-trump-ignoring-science-terrifying-launch-a8313966.html

[74] By the time he took office, Bridenstine appeared to have changed his opinion, saying he 'had no reason to doubt' the scientific conclusion that 'it is extremely likely... that human activity is the dominant cause of global warming' https://edition.cnn.com/2018/05/23/politics/nasa-administrator-hawaii-senator-climate-change/index.html

[75] https://en.wikipedia.org/wiki/Milankovitch_cycles

[76] https://www.clim-past.net/3/485/2007/cp-3-485-2007.pdf

[77] https://public.wmo.int/en/media/press-release/state-of-climate-2017-—-extreme-weather-and-high-impacts

[78] https://nca2014.globalchange.gov/report/our-changing-climate/ocean-acidification#intro-section-2

[79] https://en.wikipedia.org/wiki/Permian–Triassic_extinction_event

[80] http://www.secoteco.at/projekte/TriasKatastrophe.pdf

[81] https://www.sanluisobispo.com/news/weather/weather-watch/article39516393.html

[82] https://www.blogs.uni-mainz.de/fb09climatology/files/2012/03/Pages_2013_NatureGeo.pdf

[83] https://www2.bc.edu/jeremy-shakun/Marcott%20et%20al.,%202013,%20Science.pdf

[84] http://www.rsc.org/images/Arrhenius1896_tcm18-173546.pdf

[85] https://www.imperial.ac.uk/media/imperial-college/grantham-institute/public/publications/briefing-papers/Solar-Influences-on-Climate---Grantham-BP-5.pdf

[86] https://en.wikipedia.org/wiki/The_Chilling_Stars

[87] https://en.wikipedia.org/wiki/The_Great_Global_Warming_Swindle

[88] http://solar-center.stanford.edu/sun-on-earth/2009RG000282.pdf

[89] https://www.atmos-chem-phys.net/10/1885/2010/acp-10-1885-2010.html

[90] http://news.bbc.co.uk/1/hi/sci/tech/7327393.stm

[91]http://rspa.royalsocietypublishing.org/content/464/2094/1387

[92] https://www.carbonbrief.org/why-the-sun-is-not-responsible-for-recent-climate-change

[93] http://www.drroyspencer.com/research-articles/global-warming-as-a-natural-response/

[94]https://www.researchgate.net/publication/232750246_Anthropogenic_and_natural_warming_inferred_from_changes_in_Earth%27s_energy_balance

[95] https://journals.ametsoc.org/doi/abs/10.1175/JCLI-D-16-0803.1

[96] http://www.ipcc.ch/pdf/assessment-report/ar5/wg1/WG1AR5_Chapter08_FINAL.pdf. A 'forcing' is any factor that affects the global temperature – or indeed any other aspect of the climate

[97] https://journals.ametsoc.org/doi/10.1175/1520-0442%282004%29017%3C3721%3ACONAAF%3E2.0.CO%3B2

[98]https://en.wikipedia.org/wiki/List_of_known_large_volcanic_eruptions

[99]https://agupubs.onlinelibrary.wiley.com/doi/full/10.1029/2003GL016875. Volcanic eruptions cool the planet by putting copious quantities of dust into the atmosphere, blocking the sun's energy

[100]https://science2017.globalchange.gov/downloads/CSSR2017_FullReport.pdf

[101] https://www.carbonbrief.org/analysis-why-scientists-think-100-of-global-warming-is-due-to-humans

[102]http://www.columbia.edu/~lmp/paps/randel+polvani+etal-JGR-2017.pdf

[103]https://www.eumetsat.int/cs/idcplg?IdcService=GET_FILE&dDocName=pdf_conf_p50_s9_01_harries_v&allowInterrupt=1&noSaveAs=1&RevisionSelectionMethod=LatestReleased

[104] http://archiv.ub.uni-heidelberg.de/volltextserver/6862/1/LevinRAD2000.pdf

[105] https://en.wikipedia.org/wiki/Climate_sensitivity

[106] https://www.carbonbrief.org/explainer-how-scientists-estimate-climate-sensitivity

[107] IPCC WG1 AR5 SPM *Ibid*

[108] https://journals.ametsoc.org/doi/10.1175/JCLI-D-17-0667.1

[109]https://twitter.com/curryja/status/988752505168453632

[110]https://twitter.com/mattwridley/status/992037220147134465

[111] https://eartharxiv.org/4et67

[112]https://twitter.com/mattwridley/status/1006495814221488128

[113] https://eciu.net/briefings/climate-science-the-basics/has-climate-change-stopped

[114]https://rmets.onlinelibrary.wiley.com/doi/abs/10.1002/qj.2297

[115] https://www.nature.com/news/climate-change-hiatus-disappears-with-new-data-1.17700

[116]https://agupubs.onlinelibrary.wiley.com/doi/full/10.1029/2012GL051106 – the remaining 6% is divided equally between energy that warms the land surface, and energy that turns ice into water (latent heat)

[117]https://agupubs.onlinelibrary.wiley.com/doi/pdf/10.1002/grl.50382

[118]https://pdfs.semanticscholar.org/08f2/6af247af8580dfb975a56dc8a274febdae58.pdf

[119] https://www.metoffice.gov.uk/news/releases/2017/a-pacific-flip-triggers-the-end-of-the-recent-slowdown

[120] https://data.giss.nasa.gov/gistemp/graphs/

[121] This is a phenomenon well known to statisticians, called 'regression toward the mean' https://en.wikipedia.org/wiki/Regression_toward_the_mean

[122] https://www.carbonbrief.org/interactive-much-el-nino-affect-global-temperature

[123] *Ibid*

[124]https://twitter.com/rahmstorf/status/953939227334533120/photo/1?ref_src

[125] https://ane4bf-datap1.s3-eu-west-1.amazonaws.com/wmocms/s3fs-public/ckeditor/files/gmt_skyscraper.png?fb80cBnXm76KDaaRl30S9nOaZUEdtzuu

[126]https://www.metoffice.gov.uk/news/releases/2018/2017-temperature-announcement

[127] https://www.carbonbrief.org/analysis-how-well-have-climate-models-projected-global-warming

[128]https://www.thegwpf.org/content/uploads/2017/02/Curry-2017.pdf

[129] https://ipcc.ch/pdf/special-reports/spm/sres-en.pdf

[130] *An Appeal to Reason*, p36. These numbers refer to Lawson's calculations on the 'gloomiest' of the various IPCC scenarios; for the 'most optimistic', he calculates that people in richer nations would be 47 times better off with climate change rather than 48 times without it, while for the developing world the figures are respectively 45 times and 50 times.

[131] http://pure.iiasa.ac.at/id/eprint/12825/7/esd-7-327-2016.pdf

[132]http://www.ipcc.ch/publications_and_data/ar4/wg2/en/ch7s7-5.html

[133] http://www.ipcc.ch/pdf/assessment-report/ar5/wg2/ar5_wgII_spm_en.pdf

[134]https://www.worldweatherattribution.org/analyses/the-role-of-climate-change-in-the-2015-2017-drought-in-the-western-cape-of-south-africa/

[135]https://www.nature.com/articles/nclimate1449?cacheBust=1509955944616

[136] https://www.nature.com/articles/nclimate3357

[137]https://www.nature.com/scitable/knowledge/library/ocean-acidification-25822734

[138] http://portal.goa-on.org/Explorer

[139] https://books.google.co.uk/books?hl=en&lr=&id=P2Q-DwAAQBAJ&oi=fnd&pg=PT74&dq=ocean+acidification+impacts+on+marine+life&ots=wzZpqAW7N_&sig=znt2W

M6TzlDHcGNc5laKzQxQEuY#v=onepage&q=ocean%20acidification%20impacts%20on%20marine%20life&f=false

[140] https://ecology.wa.gov/About-us/Our-role-in-the-community/Partnerships-committees/Ocean-acidification-Blue-Ribbon-panel

[141] https://www.nature.com/articles/ngeo1635

[142] https://onlinelibrary.wiley.com/doi/pdf/10.1111/gcb.13167

[143] https://www.nature.com/articles/nature25493

[144] https://www.nature.com/articles/s41561-018-0152-2

[145] https://www.nature.com/articles/s41561-018-0152-2.epdf

[146] http://aura.abdn.ac.uk/bitstream/handle/2164/5872/GCB_proof_Baudron_et_al.pdf;sequence=1

[147] https://www.nature.com/articles/srep16293

[148] https://www.cell.com/current-biology/fulltext/S0960-9822(17)31539-7

[149] https://www.nature.com/articles/s41561-018-0152-2

[150] https://www.frontiersin.org/articles/10.3389/fmars.2016.00062/full

[151] http://www.whaleroute.com/migrate/

[152] http://www.pnas.org/content/early/2017/05/31/1701262114

[153] http://www.fao.org/documents/card/en/c/I9540EN/

[154] *An Appeal to Reason* p66

[155] *Ibid*, p42

[156] *Ibid*, p44; originally FA Hayek, *The Economy, Science, and Politics*

[157] https://www.toronto.ca/community-people/health-wellness-care/health-programs-advice/extreme-heat-and-heat-related-illness/harmonized-heat-warning-and-information-system/

[158] http://www.africarice.org/warda/uplandnerica.asp

[159] https://www.ft.com/content/40cb8f96-87ee-11e7-afd2-74b8ecd34d3b

[160]https://web.archive.org/web/20160411040314/http://blogs.telegraph.co.uk/news/jamesdelingpole/100210866/an-english-class-for-trolls-professional-offence-takers-and-climate-activists/

[161]https://insideclimatenews.org/news/15092015/Exxons-own-research-confirmed-fossil-fuels-role-in-global-warming

[162]https://www.parliament.uk/business/committees/committees-a-z/commons-select/science-and-technology-committee/inquiries/parliament-2005/uea/

[163] https://www.uea.ac.uk/about/media-room/press-release-archive/statements/cru-statements/oxburgh

[164] http://www.cce-review.org

[165] An umbrella body for countries' national science academies.

[166] https://www.bbc.co.uk/news/10506283

[167] http://news.bbc.co.uk/1/hi/world/asia-pacific/8325377.stm

[168] https://en.wikipedia.org/wiki/Andrew_Wakefield

[169] https://retractionwatch.com/category/by-subject/environmental-science/climate-change/

[170] https://en.wikipedia.org/wiki/List_of_scientific_misconduct_incidents

[171] https://www.ipcc.ch/news_and_events/docs/factsheets/FS_review_process.pdf

[172] http://www.ipcc.ch/report/ar5/syr/

[173] http://news.bbc.co.uk/1/hi/sci/tech/7092614.stm

[174] http://www.dtu.dk/english/service/phonebook/person?id=38287&tab=2&qt=dtupublicationquery

[175] https://cornwallalliance.org/about/who-we-are/

[176] https://cornwallalliance.org/2009/05/evangelical-declaration-on-global-warming/

[177] https://www.nsstc.uah.edu/users/john.christy/publications.html

[178] http://www.drroyspencer.com/research-articles/

[179] https://www.nicholaslewis.org/peer-reviewed-publications/

[180] https://www.nature.com/articles/ngeo3031

[181] https://twitter.com/ClimateOfGavin/status/910446038707777536

[182] http://www.realclimate.org/index.php/archives/2017/10/1-50c-geophysically-impossible-or-not/

[183] http://news.bbc.co.uk/1/hi/7139797.stm

[184] https://ipccreport.wordpress.com/2014/10/08/when-climate-scientists-criticise-each-other/

[185] https://www.technologyreview.com/s/403256/global-warming-bombshell/

[186] https://www.greenpeace.org/usa/global-warming/climate-deniers/koch-industries/

[187] https://wattsupwiththat.com/2011/03/06/briggs-on-berkeleys-best-plus-my-thoughts-from-my-visit-there/

[188] https://wattsupwiththat.com/2012/08/03/an-uncorrected-assumption-in-bests-station-quality-paper/

[189] https://www.bbc.co.uk/news/science-environment-15373071

[190]https://www.telegraph.co.uk/news/earth/environment/globalwarming/11395516/The-fiddling-with-temperature-data-is-the-biggest-science-scandal-ever.html

[191]http://www.realclimate.org/index.php/archives/2008/06/of-buckets-and-blogs/langswitch_lang/in/

[192] http://berkeleyearth.org/understanding-adjustments-temperature-data/

[193] https://www.carbonbrief.org/explainer-how-data-adjustments-affect-global-temperature-records

[194]https://journals.ametsoc.org/doi/abs/10.1175/JCLI3730.1

[195]https://agupubs.onlinelibrary.wiley.com/doi/full/10.1029/2008JD009916

[196]https://www1.ncdc.noaa.gov/pub/data/ushcn/v2/monthly/menne-etal2010.pdf

[197]https://agupubs.onlinelibrary.wiley.com/doi/abs/10.1029/2012JD018509

[198] https://www.scitechnol.com/2327-4581/2327-4581-1-104.pdf

[199] http://www.remss.com/research/climate/

[200] https://www.nsstc.uah.edu/climate/

[201] http://www.remss.com/blog/faq-about-v40-tlt-update/

[202] https://www.carbonbrief.org/major-correction-to-satellite-data-shows-140-faster-warming-since-1998

[203]https://www.telegraph.co.uk/comment/columnists/christopherbooker/3560380/Our-leaders-are-in-carbon-cloud-cuckoo-land.html

[204] https://cleantechnica.com/2015/03/30/greenpeace-aces-installed-renewable-forecasts-surprised/

[205] https://www.gov.uk/government/statistics/final-uk-emissions-estimates

[206]https://data.worldbank.org/indicator/NY.GDP.MKTP.KD?end=2008&locations=GB&start=1992

[207] https://www.gov.uk/government/statistics/final-uk-emissions-estimates

[208]https://en.wikipedia.org/wiki/Wind_power_in_the_United_Kingdom#Economics

[209] https://www.legislation.gov.uk/ukia/2009/70

[210]https://www.gov.uk/government/publications/autumn-budget-2017-documents/autumn-budget-2017

[211]https://data.worldbank.org/indicator/NY.GDP.MKTP.CD

[212] https://capx.co/innovation-not-subsidy-is-transforming-the-energy-market/

[213] https://eciu.net/reports/2017/blown-away

[214] https://www.ft.com/content/8633bc9e-9f1c-11e7-9a86-4d5a475ba4c5

[215]https://www.thegwpf.org/content/uploads/2016/12/CCACost-Dec16.pdf

[216]https://d3n8a8pro7vhmx.cloudfront.net/ukipdev/pages/3944/attachments/original/1495695469/UKIP_Manifesto_June2017opt.pdf?1495695469

[217] https://www.carbonbrief.org/uk-climate-change-act-costs-benefits

[218] https://www.ft.com/content/2ce7ac15-ee6e-3f9a-b427-6d34dac99ba2

[219] http://www.ukerc.ac.uk/news/government-must-act-urgently-on-power-system-flexibility-to-avoid-costs-escalating.html

[220] https://www.solar-trade.org.uk/intermittency-cost-integrating-solar-gb-power-market/

[221] https://www.gov.uk/government/publications/smart-power-a-national-infrastructure-commission-report

[222] https://www.theccc.org.uk/publication/energy-prices-and-bills-report-2017/

[223] https://www.ft.com/content/be1a0362-f689-11e5-9afe-dd2472ea263d

[224] https://www.tatasteeleurope.com/static_files/Downloads/Corporate/News/Publications/Annual%20reports/annual-report-2014-15.pdf

[225] https://www.focus-economics.com/commodities/base-metals/steel-europe

[226] https://www.parliament.uk/uk-energy-policy

[227] GWPF *ibid*

[228] https://data.worldbank.org/indicator/NY.GDP.MKTP.KD?locations=GB

[229] https://www.gov.uk/government/statistics/provisional-uk-greenhouse-gas-emissions-national-statistics-2017

[230] https://www.theccc.org.uk/2017/03/16/uk-climate-action-has-reduced-emissions-without-increases-in-household-energy-bills/

[231] https://www.ofgem.gov.uk/data-portal/electricity-generation-mix-quarter-and-fuel-source-gb

[232] https://en.wikipedia.org/wiki/Phoebus_cartel

[233] http://uk.businessinsider.com/jake-dysons-revolutionary-light-bulb-lasts-an-entire-lifetime-2016-7?r=US&IR=T

[234] https://www.theccc.org.uk/publication/reducing-uk-emissions-2018-progress-report-to-parliament/

[235] https://eciu.net/reports/2017/uk-leads-g7-in-per-capita-growth-emission-cuts

[236] UK figures (cited earlier) – 12% growth and 30% emission cuts 2008-2017. Corresponding figures for Germany are 10% and 7% - for the US, 13% and 9-10%. The US has not yet published full emission statistics for 2017, but progress to 2016 gives the 9% figure and analysts do not think a major fall will result from 2016 to 2017, hence 9-10% is fair. I have not included a Japanese comparator as its climate change progress was severely disrupted by the closure of nuclear power stations after the Fukushima disaster

[237]https://www.umweltbundesamt.de/en/publikationen/submission-under-the-united-nations-framework-3

[238]https://www.telegraph.co.uk/news/earth/energy/11169831/Britain-needs-political-climate-change-to-cut-soaring-energy-bills.html

[239] Now Chief Scientific Advisor at the Department of Business, Energy and Industrial Strategy (BEIS)

[240] http://news.bbc.co.uk/1/hi/sci/tech/4423456.stm

[241] https://eciu.net/reports/2015/the-lights-seem-to-be-staying-on-realities-behind-blackout-britain

[242] https://www.thetimes.co.uk/article/british-gas-boss-warns-of-blackout-risk-from-ofgem-investigation-p5wvndvt8f6

[243] https://eciu.net/reports/2017/overpowered-has-the-uk-paid-over-the-odds-for-energy-security

[244] https://www.ofgem.gov.uk/electricity/wholesale-market/market-efficiency-review-and-reform/electricity-market-reform/capacity-market-cm-rules

[245] https://uk.reuters.com/article/national-grid-capacity-auction-eggboroug/update-1-britains-ageing-eggborough-power-plant-to-close-idUKL8N1PS32C

[246] https://www.bbc.co.uk/news/business-38791572

[247] https://www.ofgem.gov.uk/electricity/transmission-networks/electricity-interconnectors. I include the cable connecting Britain to Northern Ireland among the four, because currently it and the Irish Republic share an island-wide electricity system

[248]https://en.wikipedia.org/wiki/Hydroelectricity_in_the_United_Kingdom

[249] https://www.theengineer.co.uk/first-new-uk-pumped-hydro-scheme-for-30-years-given-go-ahead/

[250] https://eciu.net/blog/2018/car-power

[251]https://www.iea.org/publications/freepublications/publication/Empowering_Variable_Renewables.pdf

[252] http://reports.weforum.org/global-energy-architecture-performance-index-2014/global-rankings/?doing_wp_cron=1537619558.7681438922882080078125#view/fn-10

[253] https://uk.reuters.com/article/uk-denmark-renewables-windpower/denmark-sets-record-with-43-percent-of-power-from-wind-in-2017-idUKKBN1F01VD

[254]https://publications.parliament.uk/pa/ld200708/ldhansrd/lhan159.pdf

[255] Broadly, former Soviet Union and Soviet bloc countries

[256] https://unfccc.int/sites/default/files/kpeng.pdf

[257]http://www4.unfccc.int/ndcregistry/PublishedDocuments/China%20First/China%27s%20First%20NDC%20Submission.pdf

[258] http://ec.europa.eu/eurostat/statistics-explained/index.php/Greenhouse_gas_emission_statistics_-_emission_inventories - this is to 2016, as at the time of writing the EU has not released final data for 2017

[259] http://www.ym.fi/en-us/the_environment/climate_and_air/mitigation_of_climate_change/national_climate_policy

[260] https://www.government.se/press-releases/2018/01/as-of-today-sweden-has-a-new-climate-act/

[261] https://zerocarbonact.nz/zca-summary/

[262] https://unearthed.greenpeace.org/2017/10/03/peter-oborne-the-press-has-failed-on-climate-change-jeremy-corbyn/

[263]https://www.parliament.uk/business/committees/committees-a-z/commons-select/science-and-technology-committee/news/140401-climate-report-published/

[264] https://climatefeedback.org

[265] https://www.spectator.co.uk/2018/01/revealed-the-truth-about-plastic/

[266] https://climateaudit.org

[267] https://www.nationalreview.com/planet-gore/uk-news-ccnet-ed-craig/

[268] https://en.wikipedia.org/wiki/Steve_McIntyre

[269] https://www.thegwpf.org/andrew-montford-the-climategate-inquiries/

[270]https://en.wikipedia.org/wiki/The_Great_Global_Warming_Swindle

[271]https://www.telegraph.co.uk/comment/columnists/simonheffer/6729062/Forget-climate-change-save-the-planet-from-the-thermomaniacs.html

[272]https://www.express.co.uk/comment/expresscomment/141453/Climate-change-The-most-costly-scientific-blunder-in-history

[273] http://hitchensblog.mailonsunday.co.uk/2009/11/the-inconvenient-truths-mr-gore-and-his-fanatical-friends-didnt-tell-you-about-climate-change.html

[274] https://www.spectator.co.uk/2009/11/a-wild-goose-chase/

[275] Review does not appear to be on Guardian/Observer website – accessed through Factiva

[276]https://www.theguardian.com/environment/2013/jul/26/reuters-climate-change-scepticism-coverage

[277] https://www.thetimes.co.uk/article/i-thought-of-killing-myself-says-climate-scandal-professor-q8td7pfrmrf

[278]http://www.bbc.co.uk/blogs/thereporters/richardblack/2010/07/i_didnt_know_stephen_schneider.html

[279] https://www.telegraph.co.uk/comment/7530961/Can-we-trust-the-Climategate-inquiry.html

[280] https://www.thegwpf.org/andrew-montford-the-climategate-inquiries/

[281]https://www.telegraph.co.uk/news/earth/environment/globalwarming/6636563/University-of-East-Anglia-emails-the-most-contentious-quotes.html

[282] http://www.bbc.co.uk/news/science-environment-18885500

[283]https://www.theguardian.com/environment/2009/nov/24/climate-professor-leaked-emails-uea

[284]https://www.theguardian.com/environment/2010/feb/04/climate-change-email-hacker-police-investigation

[285]http://www.bbc.co.uk/bbctrust/our_work/editorial_standards/impartiality/science_impartiality.html

[286]https://www.ipcc.ch/publications_and_data/ar4/wg2/en/ch13s13-4.html

[287] http://news.bbc.co.uk/1/hi/8488395.stm

[288] Archived at http://www.realclimate.org/docs/Leake_and_North_original_S_Times_article_31_Jan_2010.pdf

[289]http://www.realclimate.org/docs/Lewis_S_Times_PCC_Complaint_As_Sent[1].pdf

[290] https://www.thetimes.co.uk/article/the-sunday-times-and-the-ipcc-correction-wl3gdtn0g6p

[291]http://eureferendum.blogspot.co.uk/2010/01/amazongate-in-sunday-times.html

[292] http://eureferendum.blogspot.co.uk/2010/01/and-professionals-write.html

[293]https://www.telegraph.co.uk/news/earth/environment/climatechange/7111525/UN-climate-change-panel-based-claims-on-student-dissertation-and-magazine-article.html

[294]https://www.telegraph.co.uk/comment/columnists/christopherbooker/7113582/Amazongate-new-evidence-of-the-IPCCs-failures.html

[295]https://www.theguardian.com/environment/2010/aug/26/rajendra-pachauri-cleared-financial-dealings

[296] https://www.telegraph.co.uk/news/7957631/Dr-Pachauri-Apology.html

[297]

https://www.theguardian.com/media/2004/may/30/Iraqandthemedia.iraq

[298]https://twitter.com/DavidRoseUK/status/452004373246529536

[299] https://delingpoleworld.com/tag/gwpf/

[300] http://www.ipcc.ch/report/ar5/wg2/

[301] https://www.spectator.co.uk/2014/04/armageddon-averted/

[302]https://www.theguardian.com/environment/2014/mar/31/climate-change-report-ipcc-governments-unprepared-live-coverage#block-5339171de4b03f2475aef296

[303] At the time, Professor Slingo was Chief Scientist at the Met Office, while Lord Krebs chaired the Adaptation Sub-committee of the Committee on Climate Change

[304] https://www.spectator.co.uk/issues/5-december-2015/

[305] https://www.spectator.co.uk/about/

[306] https://eciu.net/press-releases/2014/survey-reveals-widespread-misconceptions-about-energy-and-climate-change

[307] Now by the Department for Business, Energy and Industrial Strategy (BEIS), which took over DECC's responsibilities after the 2015 General Election https://www.gov.uk/government/collections/public-attitudes-tracking-survey

[308] https://www.telegraph.co.uk/news/2018/04/07/uk-will-spend-trillions-reduce-co2-emissions-real-offenders/

[309] https://climateactiontracker.org/countries/china/

[310] http://www.breitbart.com/big-government/2018/05/15/delingpole-climate-change-now-even-worserer-than-evah-says-new-scientist/

[311] http://www.radiotimes.com/news/radio/2017-10-25/bbc-wrong-not-to-challenge-climate-change-sceptic-during-interview/

[312] http://www.dailymail.co.uk/sciencetech/article-4192182/World-leaders-duped-manipulated-global-warming-data.html?cmp.consent=true

[313] https://www.thetimes.co.uk/article/britain-needs-to-embrace-the-shaleenergy-revolution-vcw0bptv2

[314] https://www.carbonbrief.org/bbc-upholds-complaint-over-today-programme-nigel-lawson-interview

[315] https://www.independent.co.uk/environment/nigel-lawson-climate-change-sceptics-global-temperatures-fall-false-claim-warming-gwpf-bbc-radio-4-a7894686.html

[316]https://www.telegraph.co.uk/politics/2018/06/01/donald-trump-has-courage-wit-look-green-hysteria-say-no-deal/

[317] https://www.epa.gov/sites/production/files/2018-01/documents/2018_chapter_2_trends_in_greenhouse_gas_emissions.pdf

[318] https://www.gov.uk/government/statistics/final-uk-greenhouse-gas-emissions-national-statistics-1990-2016

[319] https://eciu.net/reports/2017/uk-leads-g7-in-per-capita-growth-emission-cuts

[320]https://www.eia.gov/energyexplained/index.php?page=electricity_in_the_united_states

[321] https://www.epa.gov/sites/production/files/2018-01/documents/2018_chapter_3_energy.pdf

[322]https://www.eia.gov/electricity/data/browser/#/topic/7?agg=0,1&geo=g&endsec=vg&linechart=ELEC.PRICE.US-ALL.M~ELEC.PRICE.US-RES.M~ELEC.PRICE.US-COM.M~ELEC.PRICE.US-IND.M&columnchart=ELEC.PRICE.US-ALL.M~ELEC.PRICE.US-RES.M~ELEC.PRICE.US-COM.M~ELEC.PRICE.US-IND.M&map=ELEC.PRICE.US-ALL.M&freq=M&start=200101&end=201803&chartindexed=1&ctype=linechart<ype=pin&rtype=s&pin=&rse=0&maptype=0

[323]https://www.eia.gov/todayinenergy/detail.php?id=37072

[324]https://wedocs.unep.org/bitstream/handle/20.500.11822/22104/EGR_2017_ch_3.pdf?sequence=1&isAllowed=y

[325] https://www.prnewswire.com/news-releases/advanced-energy-for-life-campaign-launched-to-

build-awareness-and-support-to-end-worlds-number-one-human-and-environmental-crisis-of-global-energy-poverty-247238131.html

[326] https://www.civicus.org/index.php/state-of-civil-society-report-2017

[327] https://www.thetimes.co.uk/article/africa-needs-to-be-richrather-than-green-slgbjsl62hq

[328] https://www.bp.com/content/dam/bp/en/corporate/pdf/energy-economics/statistical-review/bp-stats-review-2018-full-report.pdf

[329] Last year the UN Environment Programme found that 'In at least 10 Ogoni communities where drinking water is contaminated with high levels of hydrocarbons, public health is seriously threatened... The environmental restoration of Ogoniland could prove to be the world's most wide-ranging and long-term oil clean-up exercise ever undertaken.' https://www.unenvironment.org/news-and-stories/story/unep-ogoniland-oil-assessment-reveals-extent-environmental-contamination-and

[330] https://www.bbc.co.uk/news/world-africa-42151722

[331] https://en.wikipedia.org/wiki/Coal#World_coal_reserves

[332] https://www.sun-connect-news.org/news/details/bangladesh-solar-power-industry-is-yet-to-stand-on-its-own-feet/

[333] http://www.loopsamoa.com/business/samoan-governments-renewable-energy-drive-intensifies-76765

[334] https://en.wikipedia.org/wiki/International_Solar_Alliance

[335]https://www.iea.org/publications/freepublications/publication/WEO2014_AfricaEnergyOutlook.pdf

[336] https://www.smh.com.au/national/george-pell-set-to-face-two-trials-over-historical-assault-allegations-20180502-p4zct9.html

[337] https://www.thegwpf.org/2014-annual-gwpf-lecture-owen-paterson-keeping-the-lights-on/

[338]https://www.legislation.gov.uk/ukpga/2008/27/contents

[339]https://www.telegraph.co.uk/news/earth/energy/11157454/An-energy-policy-that-makes-little-sense.html

[340] http://www.rationaloptimist.com/blog/the-greening-of-the-planet/

[341] https://www.youtube.com/watch?v=nHBWvX9qGu0

[342] 42'10" into the lecture

[343]https://twitter.com/rupertmurdoch/status/288024961426264064

[344] https://www.thetimes.co.uk/article/now-heres-the-good-news-on-global-warming-p322w7026lv

[345] https://www.thegwpf.org/matt-ridley-global-warming-versus-global-greening/

[346] https://www.osti.gov/servlets/purl/1328357

[347] https://www.bu.edu/cas/myneni-documents-extensive-leaf-growth-worldwide-due-to-global-warming/

[348] http://sites.bu.edu/cliveg/mynenis-response-to-lord-ridleys-gwpf-talk/

[349] https://www.nature.com/articles/ncomms13428

[350] http://www.creaf.uab.es/Global-Ecology/Pdfs_UEG/2017%20NatEcolEvol.pdf

[351]http://www.pnas.org/content/pnas/114/35/9326.full.pdf

[352] http://advances.sciencemag.org/content/4/5/eaaq1012

[353] https://www.spectator.co.uk/2016/10/the-world-is-getting-greener-why-does-no-one-want-to-know/

[354]https://www.tandfonline.com/doi/ref/10.1080/01431160500033682?scroll=top

[355]http://journals.plos.org/plosone/article?id=10.1371/journal.pone.0196248

[356] https://hansard.parliament.uk/Lords/2018-01-30/debates/7A3D5643-1F2D-49C8-95CF-82B2EB72BE51/Climate-RelatedFinancialDisclosures#contribution-C33095EB-E326-4F41-8905-D8855F4B6D66

[357]https://twitter.com/mattwridley/status/960549348189798402?s=08

[358] https://academic.oup.com/reep/article-abstract/12/1/4/4804315

[359]https://twitter.com/mattwridley/status/960538907388645376

[360] https://www.ofgem.gov.uk/publications-and-updates/infographic-bills-prices-and-profits

[361] https://www.ukpower.co.uk/gas_electricity_news/uk-vs-eu-energy-prices-consumption-and-renewables

[362]https://www.telegraph.co.uk/finance/newsbysector/industry/12016939/Autumn-Statement-2015-Steel-industry-to-be-exempted-from-green-energy-taxes.html

[363] https://www.theccc.org.uk/2017/08/03/green-policies-made-9-typical-household-energy-bill-2016-ccc-analysis-shows/

[364]https://www.telegraph.co.uk/business/2017/03/23/false-claims-low-carbon-energy-damaging-uk/

[365]https://www.parliament.uk/business/committees/committees-a-z/lords-select/economic-affairs-committee/inquiries/parliament-2015/uk-energy-policy/

[366] https://www.regensw.co.uk/news/book-review-burn-out-the-endgame-for-fossil-fuels-by-dieter-helm-16-may-2017

[367] https://www.gov.uk/government/publications/cost-of-energy-independent-review page 29

[368] https://www.carbonbrief.org/house-of-lords-energy-report-slammed-confused-misleading

[369] https://www.ofgem.gov.uk/gas/retail-market/retail-market-monitoring/understanding-trends-energy-prices

[370]https://www.sciencedirect.com/science/article/pii/S0301421516301458

[371] https://www.reuters.com/article/uk-global-renewables/record-amount-of-renewable-energy-installed-in-2017-research-idUKKCN1IZ0YL

[372]https://www.sciencedirect.com/science/article/pii/S0301421517307693

[373] https://www.gov.uk/government/publications/clean-growth-strategy

[374]https://www.cps.org.uk/files/reports/original/160929100405-84AreWeHeadedforBlackoutBritain.pdf

[375] https://www.gov.uk/government/statistics/energy-and-climate-change-public-attitudes-tracker-wave-25

[376]https://assets.publishing.service.gov.uk/government/uploads/system/uploads/attachment_data/file/237330/MacKay_Stone_shale_study_report_09092013.pdf

[377] https://www.ebn.nl/wp-content/uploads/2017/11/A-Louwen_thesis_Final_PDF.pdf

[378]https://www.researchgate.net/publication/282709912_Unconventional_and_unburnable_Why_going_all_out_for_shale_gas_is_the_wrong_direction_for_the_UK%27s_energy_policy

[379] https://hansard.parliament.uk/Lords/2013-06-18/debates/13061896000391/EnergyBill?highlight=lawson%20shale%20gas#contribution-13061811200063

[380] https://www.thesun.co.uk/news/1471078/theresa-may-could-create-jobs-and-boost-economy-by-fracking/

[381] https://www.thetimes.co.uk/article/britain-needs-to-embrace-the-shaleenergy-revolution-vcw0bptv2

[382] https://www.spectator.co.uk/2015/07/britain-needs-to-get-fracking/

[383]https://en.wikipedia.org/wiki/Shippingport_Atomic_Power_Station

[384]https://en.wikipedia.org/wiki/Sellafield#Calder_Hall_nuclear_power_station

[385] https://www.rolls-royce.com/products-and-services/nuclear/small-modular-reactors.aspx

[386]https://www.forbes.com/sites/michaelshellenberger/2018/07/18/if-radical-innovation-makes-nuclear-power-expensive-why-do-we-think-it-will-make-nuclear-cheap/#26144668489f

[387] https://www.thegwpf.org/2014-annual-gwpf-lecture-owen-paterson-keeping-the-lights-on/

[388] https://eciu.net/press-releases/2018/poll-reveals-mps-misconceptions-over-onshore-wind

[389] http://www.oecd.org/dac/stats/the070dagnitarget-ahistory.htm

[390] https://eciu.net/reports/2017/blown-away

[391] https://eciu.net/blog/2015/eu-diktat-shocker

[392] https://eciu.net/press-releases/2015/oven-energy-makeover-to-slash-1-1bn-from-brits-bills

[393] *Ibid*

[394] https://eciu.net/blog/2016/uks-interest-in-eus-energy-package

[395] https://www.thegwpf.com/energy-efficiency-and-conservation-and-climate-policy-cost/

[396] https://www.thegwpf.com/energy-efficiency-lessons-from-the-green-deal-and-energy-company-obligation/

[397] https://www.thegwpf.com/the-brexit-white-paper-and-uk-energy-and-climate-policy/

[398] https://www.thegwpf.com/energy-efficiency-smart-meters-and-climate-policy/

[399] https://www.gov.uk/government/speeches/amber-rudds-speech-on-a-new-direction-for-uk-energy-policy

[400] http://www.dailymail.co.uk/debate/article-3308821/PETER-HITCHENS-Warmists-armed-windmills-REAL-threat-Britain.html

[401] https://www.telegraph.co.uk/news/earth/energy/11980548/The-obsession-with-global-warming-will-put-the-lights-out-all-over-Britain.html

[402] https://www.thetimes.co.uk/article/weve-blown-it-by-rushing-towards-wind-power-v97b6blhsco

[403] https://www.gov.uk/government/speeches/amber-rudds-speech-on-a-new-direction-for-uk-energy-policy

[404] https://www.telegraph.co.uk/news/earth/energy/11994954/Amber-Rudd-end-to-pursuit-of-green-energy-at-all-costs.html

[405] http://www.thisismoney.co.uk/money/news/article-3207201/Energy-review-spells-end-green-bandwagon-Spotlight-true-costs-power-generation-save-billions.html

[406] https://www.thetimes.co.uk/article/25-power-stations-needed-to-stop-lights-going-out-67fpqvjmqc2

[407] https://www.parliament.uk/business/committees/committees-a-z/commons-select/energy-and-climate-change-committee/news-parliament-2015/investor-confidence-report-published-15-16/

[408] Now Forsa Energy

[409] https://eciu.net/reports/2017/overpowered-has-the-uk-paid-over-the-odds-for-energy-security

[410] https://eciu.net/press-releases/2017/comment-on-nao-report-on-hinkley-point-c

[411] *The Real Global Warming Disaster*, p250

[412] https://www.heatonharris.com/campaigns/wind-energyplanning

[413] https://www.gov.uk/government/publications/cost-of-energy-independent-review

[414] http://www.bbc.co.uk/complaints/comp-reports/ecu/sixr425102017

[415] https://www.bbc.co.uk/news/business-41747264

[416] https://www.ofgem.gov.uk/publications-and-updates/infographic-bills-prices-and-profits

[417]https://www.newstatesman.com/politics/religion/2018/04/remainers-attacking-bbc-should-be-wary-ending-british-fox-news

[418]https://www.theguardian.com/environment/2014/sep/02/nigel-lawson-climate-sceptic-organisation-funders

[419] https://www.bbc.co.uk/news/science-environment-44980363

[420] https://www.nature.com/articles/nature03089

[421]https://inews.co.uk/news/politics/climate-change-john-humphrys-bbc-radio-4-today-programme/

[422]https://www.telegraph.co.uk/business/2017/02/02/bad-news-petrol-heads-trump-no-trump-green-revolution-coming/

[423] https://www.thetimes.co.uk/article/onshore-wind-farms-could-blow-in-1-6bn-of-savings-9dwn66t3d

[424] https://cleantechnica.com/2017/03/06/118005/

[425]https://www.irena.org/publications/2018/Jan/Renewable-power-generation-costs-in-2017

[426] https://www.iea.org/publications/renewables2017/

[427] https://www.wsj.com/articles/global-investment-in-wind-and-solar-energy-is-outshining-fossil-fuels-1528718400

[428] https://eciu.net/briefings/international-perspectives/is-britain-going-it-alone-on-climate-change

[429] https://endcoal.org/global-coal-plant-tracker/reports/

[430] http://ieefa.org/ieefa-china-a-sea-change-in-energy-policy/

[431] https://endcoal.org/global-coal-plant-tracker/summary-statistics/

[432] Ieefa, *Ibid*

[433]http://www.cea.nic.in/reports/committee/nep/nep_dec.pdf

[434]https://energy.economictimes.indiatimes.com/news/power/thermal-power-plants-capacity-utilisation-to-drop-to-48-by-2022/56075578?redirect=1

[435] https://www.reuters.com/article/us-usa-energy-coal-closures/coal-plant-closures-continue-even-as-u-s-ends-clean-power-plan-idUSKBN1CI2RH

[436] https://endcoal.org/global-coal-plant-tracker/reports/

[437] https://endcoal.org/global-coal-plant-tracker/reports/

[438] http://www.ipcc.ch/report/sr15/

[439] https://www.bbc.co.uk/news/world-latin-america-11533349

[440]https://www.sciencedirect.com/science/article/pii/S2300396017300551

[441]http://www.who.int/mediacentre/news/releases/2014/air-pollution/en/

[442] http://thehill.com/opinion/energy-environment/369823-data-shows-solar-energy-really-is-a-leading-american-job-creator?utm

[443] https://www.reuters.com/article/us-usa-coal-jobs/exclusive-trumps-coal-job-push-stumbles-in-most-states-data-idUSKBN1F81AK

[444]https://www.gov.uk/government/statistics/beis-public-attitudes-tracker-wave-26

[445] https://eciu.net/press-releases/2017/survey-reveals-britons-support-for-climate-legislation

[446] https://eciu.net/press-releases/2017/85-of-britons-back-subsidies-for-renewables

[447] https://www.gov.uk/government/statistics/energy-and-climate-change-public-attitudes-tracker-wave-25

[448] *Ibid*

[449] http://www.ipcc.ch/report/ar5/wg2/

[450] http://www.ipcc.ch/report/ar5/syr/

[451] https://eciu.net/blog/2017/truth-in-brandy-trump-is-a-remainer

[452]http://www.climatechangenews.com/2018/10/26/bolsonaro-says-brazil-will-stay-paris-agreement/

[453] https://www.shell.com/energy-and-innovation/the-energy-future/scenarios/shell-scenario-sky.html

[454] https://www.bp.com/en/global/corporate/energy-economics/energy-outlook/carbon-emissions.html

[455]https://www.total.com/sites/default/files/atoms/files/integrating_climate_into_our_strategy_va.pdf

[456] http://news.exxonmobil.com/press-release/exxonmobil-releases-energy-carbon-summary-and-outlook-energy

[457] http://climatecasechart.com/?cn-reloaded=1

[458] http://vision2030.gov.sa/en

[459] https://gulfnews.com/culture/environment/gulf-will-be-too-hot-for-humans-by-2070-study-1.1608055

[460] https://www.moneysupermarket.com/car-insurance/electric-car/the-cost-of-driving-green/

[461] https://www.ft.com/content/7bbd9a9a-1326-11e8-940e-08320fc2a277

[462] https://cleantechnica.com/2017/11/23/6-10-big-electric-car-companies-china/

[463] https://about.bnef.com/blog/breakneck-rise-chinas-colossus-electric-car-batteries/

[464] https://cleantechnica.com/2018/10/08/teslas-battery-in-south-australia-breaks-stranglehold-of-natural-gas-industry/

[465]https://www.telegraph.co.uk/comment/11155315/Global-warming-Can-Owen-Paterson-save-us-from-an-unimaginable-energy-disaster.html

[466]https://www.telegraph.co.uk/news/earth/energy/11156113/Scrap-the-Climate-Change-Act-to-keep-the-lights-on-says-Owen-Paterson.html

[467]https://www.telegraph.co.uk/news/earth/energy/11157454/An-energy-policy-that-makes-little-sense.html

[468]https://www.telegraph.co.uk/news/earth/energy/11163094/Climate-change-forecasts-exaggerated-ex-environment-secretary-Owen-Paterson-claims.html

[469]https://www.telegraph.co.uk/news/earth/energy/11169831/Britain-needs-political-climate-change-to-cut-soaring-energy-bills.html

[470]https://www.telegraph.co.uk/news/politics/conservative/11171315/Owen-Paterson-Lets-put-our-energy-into-winning-back-small-c-conservatives.html

[471]https://www.telegraph.co.uk/news/earth/energy/11175813/Fantasy-policies-will-not-solve-our-energy-crisis.html

[472] http://uksif.org/2018/04/26/energy-transition-risk-will-dent-oil-company-valuations-within-5-years-predict-89-of-fund-managers/

[473] https://www.thegwpf.com/who-we-are/board-of-trustees/

[474] http://www.recordcm.com/wp-content/uploads/2018/04/Record-Currency-Management-ESG-Policy-v3.pdf

[475] https://www.bbc.co.uk/news/science-environment-44980363

[476] https://www.thegwpf.com/hoskins-vs-lawson-the-climate-debate-the-bbc-wants-to-censor/

[477] http://www.ipcc.ch/pdf/assessment-report/ar5/wg1/WG1AR5_SPM_FINAL.pdf, pages 6-7:

'Changes in many extreme weather and climate events have been observed since about 1950. It is *very likely* that the number of cold days and nights has decreased and the number of warm days and nights has increased on the global scale. It is *likely* that the frequency of heat waves has increased in large parts of Europe, Asia and Australia. There are *likely* more land regions where the number of heavy precipitation events has increased than where it has decreased. The frequency or intensity of heavy precipitation events has *likely* increased in North America and Europe. In other continents, *confidence* in changes in heavy precipitation events is at most *medium*.'

[478] The document in question is http://www.metoffice.gov.uk/media/pdf/m/8/A3_plots-precip-DJF-2.pdf, which states: 'Confidence in the forecast for precipitation across the UK over the next three months is relatively low. For the December-January-February period as a whole there is a slight signal for below-average precipitation. The probability that UK precipitation for December-January-February will fall into the driest of our five categories is around 25%, and the probability that it will fall into the wettest category is around 15%.' This cannot be reasonably be interpreted as 'forecasting a dry winter'

[479]http://www.bbc.co.uk/helpandfeedback/corrections_clarifications/corrections_july_2014.html

[480] http://www.dailymail.co.uk/debate/article-2685405/Ive-banned-BBC-Ex-Chancellor-Lord-Lawson-passionate-climate-change-sceptic-accuses-BBC-bosses-silencing-debate-global-warming.html

[481] https://www.spectator.co.uk/2014/07/climatic-correctness/

[482] https://www.carbonbrief.org/oecd-fossil-fuel-subsidies-373-billion-2015

[483]https://www.sciencedirect.com/science/article/pii/S0305750X16304867

[484] http://iopscience.iop.org/article/10.1088/1748-9326/aa9663/meta

[485] https://www.independent.co.uk/environment/nigel-lawson-climate-change-sceptics-global-temperatures-fall-false-claim-warming-gwpf-bbc-radio-4-a7894686.html

[486]https://www.bbc.co.uk/programmes/b00k8fmc/episodes/player

[487] http://www.bbc.co.uk/editorialguidelines/guidelines/

[488]https://www.theguardian.com/environment/2015/aug/05/whats-the-point-of-bbc-editorial-guidelines-climate-change

[489] https://www.thegwpf.org/who-we-are/board-of-trustees/

[490]http://downloads.bbc.co.uk/bbctrust/assets/files/pdf/appeals/esc_bulletins/2015/met_office.pdf

[491] https://www.carbonbrief.org/exclusive-bbc-issues-internal-guidance-on-how-to-report-climate-change

[492]https://www.theguardian.com/commentisfree/2018/sep/10/bbc-climate-change-deniers

[493] http://eciu.net/blog/2015/there-is-a-point-to-bbc-editorial-guidelines

[494] http://www.dailymail.co.uk/debate/article-3187587/What-shower-money-Met-Office-gets-ludicrously-inaccurate-doom-mongering-climate-change.html

[495] IPSO replaced the Press Complaints Commission in 2014 following the Leveson Inquiry

[496] https://www.ipso.co.uk/rulings-and-resolution-statements/ruling/?id=00894-17

[497] http://www.dailymail.co.uk/news/article-4913782/IPSO-upholds-complaint-Max-Hill-QC-against-MoS.html

[498] http://www.dailymail.co.uk/sciencetech/article-4192182/World-leaders-duped-manipulated-global-warming-data.html

[499] http://science.sciencemag.org/content/348/6242/1469

[500] http://www.lse.ac.uk/GranthamInstitute/news/the-mail-on-sunday-forced-to-acknowledge-it-published-fake-news-about-climate-change/

[501] http://www.dailymail.co.uk/sciencetech/article-4192182/World-leaders-duped-manipulated-global-warming-data.html

[502] http://www.dailymail.co.uk/home/article-5642887/Clarifications-corrections.html

[503] http://www.britishinfrastructuregroup.uk/wp-content/uploads/2016/12/Electric-Shock-will-the-Xmas-lights-go-out.pdf

[504] https://twitter.com/BIG_MPs

[505] https://www.cps.org.uk/publications/are-we-heading-for-blackout-britain/

[506]https://www.theguardian.com/environment/2016/dec/19/campaigners-dismiss-christmas-electricity-blackout-report-as-laughable

[507]https://www.scribd.com/document/309807683/Letter-to-the-Times-re-climate-change-coverage

[508]https://www.thetimes.co.uk/edition/comment/climate-change-lobby-wants-to-kill-free-speech-l975jdxp8

[509] https://www.thegwpf.com/matt-ridley-climate-change-lobby-wants-to-kill-free-speech/

[510] Not locatable on *The Times* website, but reproduced here http://bishophill.squarespace.com/blog/2016/4/29/the-liberal-society-and-its-publicly-funded-enemies.html

[511]https://www.telegraph.co.uk/news/2018/01/06/americas-deep-freeze-weather-bomb-nothing-new-proves-still/

[512]https://www.telegraph.co.uk/science/2018/01/20/global-warming-theorists-tripping-explain-americas-cold-winters/

[513]https://notalotofpeopleknowthat.wordpress.com/2018/01/04/alarmists-wheel-out-record-cold-due-to-global-warming-argument-again/

[514]https://notalotofpeopleknowthat.wordpress.com/2018/01/15/us-cold-winters-mysteriously-disappear/

[515]https://notalotofpeopleknowthat.wordpress.com/2018/01/29/greenland-is-getting-colder-new-study/

[516]https://notalotofpeopleknowthat.wordpress.com/2018/04/20/greenland-no-warmer-now-than-the-1880s/

[517]https://www.telegraph.co.uk/news/2018/03/03/despite-brexiteer-wishful-thinking-no-easy-way-ireland-impasse/

[518]https://www.telegraph.co.uk/news/2018/05/27/unravelling-real-story-behind-grenfell-tragedy-should-tackled/

[519] https://www.telegraph.co.uk/news/2018/06/09/1979-documentary-jeremy-thorpe-shows-far-bbc-has-fallen/

[520]https://www.telegraph.co.uk/news/2017/07/15/donald-trump-took-heat-rest-g20s-posturing-wont-hide-rising/

[521]https://www.telegraph.co.uk/news/2017/07/15/donald-trump-took-heat-rest-g20s-posturing-wont-hide-rising/

[522]https://www.telegraph.co.uk/opinion/2016/04/16/global-governance-is-making-the-eu-irrelevant/

[523]https://twitter.com/DrSimEvans/status/1018808554353053697

[524]https://notalotofpeopleknowthat.wordpress.com/2018/06/13/why-the-sun-controls-the-climate-and-co2-is-meaningless/

[525]https://notalotofpeopleknowthat.wordpress.com/2018/08/15/bob-ward-complains-to-ipso-and-loses/

[526]https://notalotofpeopleknowthat.wordpress.com/2018/02/11/more-fake-news-from-jillian-ambrose/

[527] https://www.thetimes.co.uk/article/charles-clover-on-the-evil-twin-of-climate-change-pznf7ng55dx

[528]http://www.bbc.co.uk/blogs/thereporters/richardblack/2009/12/cop15_questions_about_sex.html

[529]https://www.americanprogress.org/issues/green/reports/2009/05/19/6042/global-warmings-six-americas/

[530] https://www.thegwpf.org/who-we-are/board-of-trustees/

[531] https://www.thegwpf.org/who-we-are/academic-advisory-council/

[532]https://notalotofpeopleknowthat.wordpress.com/2016/10/26/emily-gosden-spins-the-ieas-misleading-propaganda/

[533]https://notalotofpeopleknowthat.wordpress.com/2017/02/27/little-emilys-replacement-no-better/

[534]https://notalotofpeopleknowthat.wordpress.com/2018/02/11/more-fake-news-from-jillian-ambrose/

[535]https://notalotofpeopleknowthat.wordpress.com/2018/08/18/wind-power-is-free-says-silly-little-telegraph-reporter/

[536]https://www.theguardian.com/environment/2014/feb/12/nigel-lawson-met-office-floods-global-warming

[537] http://www.breitbart.com/london/2016/10/18/matt-ridley-climate-change-lecture/

[538] http://delingpoleworld.com/2010/09/14/why-from-now-on-im-flying-ryanair/

[539] https://www.macleans.ca/opinion/on-climate-barbie-and-the-plight-of-the-man-un-laughed-with/

[540] https://hansard.parliament.uk/Commons/2015-01-16/debates/15011660000005/ControlOfOffshoreWindTurbinesBill

[541] http://www.dailymail.co.uk/news/article-5850939/Calls-Sir-Christopher-Chope-sacked-stripped-knighthood-upskirting-bill-block.html

[542] http://fieldrecruitment.co.uk/jobs/?pageType=single_job&job_id=4123848

[543] https://www.scribd.com/document/293004226/Email-from-Benny-to-UK-press-on-Paris-Climate-COP21-Taks

[544] https://www.thetimes.co.uk/article/this-anti-science-madness-has-got-to-stop-5hjgvlfxr

[545] https://www.dailymail.co.uk/news/article-6064961/MICHAEL-HOWARD-says-summer-proves-Margaret-Thatcher-right.html

[546] https://www.breitbart.com/london/2018/08/17/delingpole-margaret-thatcher-would-have-backed-trump-on-climate/

[547] https://notalotofpeopleknowthat.wordpress.com/2018/08/16/michael-howard-loses-the-plot/

[548] https://twitter.com/RupertDarwall/status/981564069302931456

[549] https://www.telegraph.co.uk/news/2018/08/08/strong-conservative-case-made-global-warming/

[550] https://www.thetimes.co.uk/article/green-growth-5s2kz6k3w

[551] http://www.dailymail.co.uk/news/article-4406668/Crackdown-energy-rip-offs.html

[552] https://www.thetimes.co.uk/article/left-or-right-remain-or-leave-we-are-united-in-wanting-a-cleaner-greener-future-for-our-children-09dl5cxws

[553] https://www.theclimatecoalition.org/joint-letter/

[554]https://petition.parliament.uk/archived/petitions/42784

[555] https://www.change.org/p/uk-parliament-stop-expensive-eu-renewable-energy-targets-in-the-uk

[556] https://www.change.org/p/stop-the-desecration-of-fenton-great-war-memorial-1914-1918

[557] https://www.change.org/p/lambeth-council-southbank-centre-boris-johnson-arts-council-england-stop-the-relocation-of-the-southbank-skate-park

[558]https://www.thegwpf.org/content/uploads/2018/02/Groupthink.pdf

[559] https://www.scribd.com/document/292508993/Matt-Ridley-interviewed-by-Roger-Harrabin

[560] http://science.sciencemag.org/content/325/5948/1652

[561]https://www.globalccsinstitute.com/projects/sleipner%C2%A0co2-storage-project

[562] https://climateactiontracker.org/countries/china/

[563] https://www.independent.co.uk/news/uk/home-news/most-trusted-celebrities-david-attenborough-tom-hanks-michelle-obama-piers-morgan-boris-johnson-a8143096.html

[564] http://www.itv.com/news/2018-04-16/the-queen-reveals-new-project-queens-commonwealth-canopy/

[565]https://www.theguardian.com/commentisfree/2018/apr/18/commonwealth-global-climate-change-new-zealanders

[566] https://www.thelocal.se/20170203/swedens-deputy-pm-trolls-trump-in-abortion-order-image-parody

[567]https://www.theguardian.com/environment/2018/apr/17/to-lead-on-climate-countries-must-commit-to-zero-emissions

[568] https://brightblue.org.uk/climate-change-chogm/

[569]https://www.telegraph.co.uk/business/2018/04/17/uk-path-zero-carbon-economy/

[570]https://twitter.com/RupertDarwall/status/989425594063519744

[571]https://assets.publishing.service.gov.uk/government/uploads/system/uploads/attachment_data/file/700496/clean-growth-strategy-correction-april-2018.pdf page 142

[572]https://assets.publishing.service.gov.uk/government/uploads/system/uploads/attachment_data/file/695626/Press_Notice_March_2018.pdf

[573] https://www.margaretthatcher.org/document/107346

Index

Aaronovitch, David 252
Abbott, Tony 95, 167, 194
Adaptation (to climate change) 79-82, 85-9, 154-6, 202
Aerosols 64-5
Africa and fossil fuels 144, 165-7
'AIDS denial' 23
Air pollution29, 47, 106, 167, 192, 200, 220, 236
Allen, Myles 98
'AmazonGate' 145-8, 159
Ambrose, Jillian 247-9
An Appeal to Reason 17, 19-20, 34, 49, 74, 76, 79-80, 86-7, 114, 125
Antarctic 53-4, 82, 193
Arctic 33, 53, 72, 260
- sea ice 11, 53, 83, 98, 193, 204, 264

ARGO float network 55, 101
Arrhenius, Svante 60
Attenborough, David 232, 261

Bagla, Pallava 41-2
Bali Roadmap 32, 35, 37, 44
Ball, Philip 137
BBC
- Business Unit coverage of energy 204-8
- editorial guidelines 237
- Jones Review of science coverage 143
- Today Programme interviews with Nigel Lawson 204, 210, 233-7, 239
- What's the Point Of... 237-240

Berkeley Earth Project 52, 99-101

'Big Six' energy utilities 118, 207, 237
Biomass 153, 189, 265-6
Black, Conrad 41

'Blackout Britain' scare story ('the lights will go out') 18, 23, 105, 117-122, 124, 157, 168, 181, 190, 195, 198-9, 201, 205, 207, 228-9, 241-3, 252
Black's Whitewash 140
Blair, Tony 30, 35, 134, 257
Booker, Christopher 28, 41, 46, 100-1, 103, 105, 137, 140, 144, 149-53, 161, 201, 209, 228, 239-40, 246-7, 256-61, 263-4
British Gas 118
British Infrastructure Group 241-3
Brown, Gordon 30, 32, 37, 45, 134
Bush, George W 30, 34, 134

Cameron, David 32-3, 199, 227, 229, 257
Capacity Market 121-2
CarbonBrief 110, 246
Carbon capture and storage 95, 184, 195, 219, 256
Carbon sinks 64, 173
Centre for Policy Studies 178, 181, 243
Chilling Stars, The 62
China (energy and climate policies) 13, 45, 47, 95, 126-9, 159, 217, 223, 225-6, 274
Chope, Christopher 233, 250
Christy, John 97, 103
Ciais, Phillippe 172
Clark, Ross 134, 145
Clarke, Simon 254
Climate Change Act (UK) 18, 24, 28, 33-5, 105, 107-8, 110, 113-6, 129-30, 133, 168, 194, 221, 227-9, 250, 254, 269
Climate models 46, 67-8, 136, 174-6

- ‘running too hot’ 70-4

Climate sensitivity 68-70, 74, 263, 273
Clover, Charles 247-8
Coal

- Asia 21, 44-5, 47, 134, 198, 217-8, 229
- global decline 13-4, 21, 95, 220
- health impacts 220
- lobbying 116, 164-5
- UK phase-out 107, 116, 121-2, 181, 269
- US 13, 15, 163, 184, 214-5, 218

Cogley, Graham 42
Combined heat and power (CHP) 169, 189
Committee on Climate Change 34, 129, 155, 178, 254
Constable, John 27
Contracts for Difference 109, 266
Copenhagen climate summit 17, 20, 37-9, 42-5, 48, 126-7, 133, 138, 142-4, 150, 202, 247, 250

- Copenhagen Accord 43, 45, 126

Coral 13, 75, 82-4
Cowtan and Way 71
Curry, Judith 74

Daily Express 41, 50, 137, 196
Daily Telegraph 41, 89, 117, 133, 137, 151, 157, 162, 168, 178, 198, 205, 213, 228-30, 242, 247, 249-50, 253-4
Darwall, Rupert 6, 178, 253, 262
Davies, David 233
Deben, Lord (John) 34
Delingpole, James 89, 137, 153, 156-7, 161, 184, 209, 239, 249-50, 253, 259, 263
Demand shifting (demand-side response) 123, 188-9, 226, 230
Doyle, Alister 140

Economics of climate change 30-1, 74-7, 88, 176-7, 215
Economist, The 205
Electric cars 13, 45, 128, 193, 214, 225-6
ENSO/El Niño/La Niña 21, 36, 47, 51-2, 72-3, 178, 268
Energy and Climate Change Committee 200
Energy bills 23,25, 118, 177-80, 195-7, 199, 267
- UK 'cripplingly high' 112-3, 221
- UK falling 114, 169, 179, 206, 229
- US rising 164

Energy efficiency 24, 114, 121, 163, 169, 178, 180, 186, 188-9, 195, 197, 206, 219-20, 232, 268
- Green Deal 220

Energy storage 21, 111-2, 123, 184, 195, 226, 230
European Union (energy and climate policies) 47, 107, 125-6, 129, 196-7
- EcoDesign 196
- 2030 197

Evans-Pritchard, Ambrose 205
Evans, Simon 246
Extreme weather events (and climate change) 20, 53, 67, 234, 236, 253, 257
- Cape Town drought 78
- Storm Desmond 236
- 2018 European heatwave 232

Field, Chris 154
Financial Times 109, 205, 230, 248
Flexibility mechanisms 112, 121, 123, 267, 270
Fossil fuel subsidies 210, 236
Fourier, Joseph 192
Friends of the Earth 33, 211

Germany (energy and climate policies) 107, 116, 124, 163
Glaciers 11,50, 54, 72, 172, 193, 263, 270

‘Global greening’ 170-176, 256
‘Global warming slowdown’ (also hiatus, pause) 21, 35-6, 45-7, 70-2, 74, 90, 134, 136, 141, 178, 232, 241, 257, 268
Gore, Al 28, 46, 104
Gosden, Emily 227, 248-9
Gray, Louise 249
Gray, Richard 148-50
Great Extinction Events 58
Great Global Warming Swindle, The 62, 137
Greenland ice sheet 53-4, 59, 68, 78
Greenpeace 21, 106, 132, 167, 211
Group-think 256-261
Grubb, Michael 98
Guardian, The 147, 209, 237-9
GWPF (Global Warming Policy Foundation & Forum) 16-7, 27, 40-1, 74, 110, 113, 135-6, 138, 140, 153, 156, 162, 167, 170-2, 174, 179, 189, 197, 207, 211-2, 228, 230, 237-8, 245, 252, 255-6, 259, 264

HadCRUT temperature record 35, 39, 52, 70-1, 100, 237
Haigh, Joanna 249
Halligan, Liam 229
Hamilton, Neil 41
Hausfather, Zeke 101
Hayek, Friedrich 87-8
Heaton-Harris, Chris 202
Heffer, Simon 137
Helm, Dieter 179, 206, 268
Henley, Lord (Oliver) 175-6
Hitchens, Peter 137, 198
‘Hockey stick’ 28, 46, 89, 99
Holliday, Steve 122
Holocene Climate Optimum 58-60
Homewood, Paul 246-7, 249, 253, 259

Hope, Christopher 228
Hoskins, Brian 233, 235
House of Lords Economic Affairs Committee 113, 178-9, 264, 268
Howard, John 194
Howard, Lord (Michael) 253
Hulatt, Chris 200
Humphreys, John 213
Hutton, John 201

Ice Age/interglacial transition 57-8, 69
India (energy and climate policies) 44-5, 128-9, 134, 167, 216-7, 223, 257, 274
Independent Press Standards Organisation 240-1
Interconnectors 121, 123
Intergovernmental Panel on Climate Change 6, 45-6, 51, 63, 69, 73, 76-7, 89-90, 93-7, 104, 134, 145-50, 152, 176, 192, 219, 222, 234, 246

- Fourth assessment report 31, 74
- Fifth assessment report 69-70, 76, 127, 173
- Himalaya glacier melt error 42-3, 91, 138, 145-7
- Reviews of 91, 140, 153-6
- Special report on the 1.5°C target 98, 208, 219, 222

International Solar Alliance 167

Jenkin, Bernard 254
Johnston, Philip 254
Jones, Phil 39, 140-2

King, David 45
Kinver, Mark 39
Krebs, Lord (John) 155, 245
Kyoto Protocol 30, 32, 42, 125

Laidlaw, Sam 118
Lawson, Dominic 150, 152, 208
Lawson, Nigel 16-9, 26, 28, 31, 34, 37, 40-1, 46, 69, 74-80, 84, 86-8, 106-7, 114, 125-6, 129-30, 132, 138, 144, 150, 160-2, 179, 204, 210, 233, 235-41, 249, 253, 255, 259
Leake, Jonathan 146-7
Lee, Andrew 200
Lefort, Rebecca 148-50
Letts, Quentin 212, 237-8, 240
Lewis, Nic 97
Lewis, Simon 146-8
Lilley, Lord (Peter) 110-5, 132, 238, 240, 264
Lomborg, Bjorn 164, 209, 259
Loughhead, John 117
Lovelock, James 54
Lövin, Isabella 261
'Lukewarmery' 67-70, 74, 79, 170, 173-4, 205

Mahoney, Daniel 241
Mail on Sunday 137, 152, 157, 161, 198, 240-1
Mangan, Lucy 249
Marshall, Jonathan 109
Maslowski, Wieslaw 98
May, Lord (Bob) 245
McIntyre, Steve 135
Mediaeval Warm Period 58-9
Met Office (UK) 35, 72, 102, 155, 234, 237-40, 246, 249
Milankovitch Cycles 57, 60, 64
MMR vaccine controversy 22-3, 93
Monckton, Christopher 150, 194
Montford, Andrew 140
Moore, Charles 117, 152, 156, 162-4, 198, 209, 229, 259
Muller, Richard 99, 100
Murdoch, Rupert 171-2

Myneni, Ranga 170-5

NASA temperature record 35, 52, 100
National Grid 119-123, 242
National Post 41
Neil, Andrew 252, 267
Nelson, Fraser 157
Net zero 125, 130, 219, 222, 228, 254, 262
New Economics Foundation 196
New Scientist 42
New Statesman 210
New Zealand (energy and climate policies) 130
NOAA temperature record 35, 52, 71, 100, 240-1, 256
North, Richard 145-51, 246
Nuclear fusion 182, 188
Nuclear power 107, 109, 117-8, 120-1, 185, 187, 201, 205, 216, 219-20, 224, 227, 270, 274

- Calder Hall 186
- Hinkley Point C 185-6, 201
- Rolls-Royce 186-7
- Shippingport 186
- small modular reactors182, 185-7, 190, 228, 256, 265, 269-71

Oborne, Peter 132-3, 144, 157
Ocean acidification 11, 50, 55, 58, 60, 75, 77, 81-4, 157, 193
Ocean hypoxia 82-4
Outsourcing (of commentary) 152-3, 155-7, 245-7

Pachauri, Rajendra 31, 42, 149-51, 246
Pacific Multidecadal Oscillation 63
Painter, James 26
Paris climate summit 78, 127, 156, 161, 164, 167, 214, 252

- Paris Agreement 15, 42, 123, 125, 127-8, 130, 162, 208, 214-5, 219, 221-3, 254, 257, 269, 272

Paterson, Owen 167-9, 188-9, 227-30, 233
Peiser, Benny 17, 36, 135, 138, 156, 252
Pell, Cardinal George 167
Pfeifer, Sylvia 248
Phillips, Melanie 209, 248
Philpott, Tim 243
Plimer, Ian 4, 17, 56, 259
Press Complaints Commission 147
Puttnam, Lord (David) 34

Real Global Warming Disaster, The 46, 137, 259
Record, Neil 230
Renewable energy 12, 18, 27, 47, 117, 120, 122, 124, 160, 163, 167-8, 180-1, 188, 190, 205-7, 216, 219, 224, 227, 230

- 'hidden costs' 22, 111, 199
- jobs 220
- price 13-4, 21, 45, 105-7, 128, 134, 216
- public opinion 24, 157-8, 211, 221, 255

Repeal the Act 254
Reuters 119, 140, 205
Ridley, Matt 28, 67, 69-70, 88, 132, 152-6, 161, 165, 167, 169-77, 184-5, 189-90, 198, 209, 243, 245, 256, 259-60, 265
Rifkind, Hugo 155, 252
Robinson, Nick 210, 211, 255
Rose, David 152-3, 161, 189, 240-1, 256
RSPB 33, 211, 232
Rudd, Amber 198

Sanderson, Ben 98
Sands, Sarah 212, 255
Satellite temperature record 63, 97, 102-4, 252

Saudi Arabia 32, 43, 95, 104, 142, 223-4
Schmidt, Gavin 98
Shale gas 118, 120, 162-3, 182-6, 188, 218, 230, 265, 270-1
- public opinion 188, 221

Shapps, Grant 242-3
Shellenberger, Mike 187-8
Shuckburgh, Emily 249
Slingo, Julia 155, 249
Spectator, The 56, 132, 134, 137, 153-7, 174, 185, 212, 235, 237, 248, 251-3
Spencer, Roy 63, 97, 103
Stern Review 30, 32, 35, 108, 133-4, 215
StormFront 140
Stringer, Graham 238, 240
Sun (as driver of climate change) 61-3
Sun, The 153, 157, 184, 195-6, 243, 253
Sunday Telegraph 41, 100, 105, 140, 148, 150-2, 157, 228, 245-7, 253
Sunday Times 23, 146-8, 150-2, 157, 247
Svensmark, Henrik 62, 96
Sweden (energy and climate policies) 107, 130, 261-2

Tata Steel 112
10:10 (campaign group) 206
Thatcher, Margaret 6, 16, 254, 274-5
Thomas, Nathalie 248
Times, The 28, 41, 152, 157, 170-1, 185, 198, 242, 244-5, 248-9, 252
Tol, Richard 176-7
Trenberth, Kevin 45
Trump, Donald 13-4, 162, 208, 214, 218, 222-3, 249, 261
Turnbull, Lord (Andrew) 113, 135, 170

University of East Anglia (UEA) email controversy 39, 90, 99, 127, 138, 140-4
- inquiries into 90-1, 139-40

Urban heat island effect 101-2

Volcanic eruptions 52, 64-5

Wadhams, Peter 98
Wall St Journal 170-1, 194, 216
Ward, Bob 241
Warner, Jeremy 214-6, 230
Watts, Anthony 99-102, 259
'Whataboutery' 193, 263
Witherow, John 244
WWF 42, 146-8, 167, 211

Yeo, Tim 34

Zero Carbon Homes 195

The Real Press

If you enjoyed this book, take a look at the other books we have on our list at www.therealpress.co.uk